Scott Foresman

Grade 2
Unit and End-of-Year
Benchmark Tests
Teacher's Manual

Reading STREET

Grade 2

PEARSON

Scott Foresman

Editorial Offices: Glenview, Illinois • Parsippany, New Jersey • New York, New York
Sales Offices: Boston, Massachusetts • Duluth, Georgia • Glenview, Illinois
Coppell, Texas • Sacramento, California • Mesa, Arizona

This work is protected by United States copyright laws and is provided
solely for the use of teachers and administrators in teaching courses
and assessing student learning in their classes and schools.
Dissemination or sale of any part of this work (including the World
Wide Web) will destroy the integrity of the work and is not permitted.

ISBN: 0-328-19670-3

Copyright © Pearson Education, Inc.

10 V031 14 13 12 11 10 09

Contents

OVERVIEW

Scott Foresman Reading Street provides a wide array of formal tests and classroom assessments to support instruction. Formal assessments include the following:

- Baseline Group Tests
- Weekly Selection Tests
- Fresh Reads for Differentiated Test Practice
- Unit and End-of-Year Benchmark Tests

This Teacher's Manual provides information for administering the Benchmark Tests, scoring the tests, and interpreting the results. Detailed information about other assessment materials and procedures may be found in the *Assessment Handbook*.

Description of the Benchmark Tests

In Grade 2, there are six Unit Benchmark Tests—one for each unit—and an End-of-Year Test. The Unit Benchmark Tests are designed to measure a child's progress based on the comprehension skills and strategies; theme; types of writing; phonics skills; high-frequency words; and grammar, usage, and mechanics skills taught in each unit. The End-of-Year Benchmark Test measures skills covered in all six units. The Benchmark Tests offer an integrated approach to assessment by measuring all skills and strategies in relation to reading passages.

In addition, the Benchmark Tests are designed to provide practice in test-taking skills and to prepare children to take the Reading/Language Arts section of standardized tests, state tests, or teacher-made tests. The tests include both multiple-choice and constructed-response questions. They also include writing prompts that will help children prepare for state writing tests.

Each Unit Benchmark Test has these features:

- Each test has two components—the Reading component (Parts 1–4) and the Writing component (Part 5).

- Reading–Part 1 presents two passages in different genres. The genres of the passages, drawn from fiction and nonfiction, reflect the focus genres taught in each unit.

- Each passage reflects the theme of the unit.

- Reading – Parts 1–4 contains forty multiple-choice questions and two constructed-response questions. These questions test reading comprehension; literary skills and genre; critical thinking skills; high-frequency words; phonics skills; and grammar, usage, and mechanics skills. Some of the items measure the ability to synthesize information and to compare and contrast across texts.

- Writing – Part 5 of each test presents a writing prompt based on one of the types of writing taught in the unit. These prompts are similar to those found in state writing tests.

The End-of-Year Benchmark Test follows the same design as the Unit Benchmark Tests, but it has more items. It measures selected skills from all six units taught during the year.

The Benchmark Tests are designed to assess a child's progress at the end of each unit and at the end of the school year. Passages and questions in the Unit Benchmark Tests become progressively more difficult from Unit 1 to Unit 6, to reflect the increasing sophistication of materials children are able to handle.

ADMINISTERING THE TESTS

The Benchmark Tests are designed for group administration. You may decide to administer each test in one sitting, or you may administer parts of the test in two or more sittings. (If you administer the test in two or more sittings, try to schedule the sittings on the same day or within a day of the previous sitting because some of the questions at the end of the test compare and contrast passages.)

These tests were also designed to give teachers the option of separating multiple-choice questions from the constructed-response questions. You may opt to remove or have children skip the constructed-response questions in order to create an all multiple-choice test.

These tests are not intended to be timed. We recommend allowing ample time for all children to complete the tests at their own pace. However, for the purposes of scheduling, planning, and practicing timed-test situations, the chart below shows the number of items in each test part and the estimated amount of time required to complete each section.

Unit	Test Part	Number of Items	Estimated Time
1–6	Reading – Part 1 (Passage 1)	8 multiple-choice items	15–20 minutes
		1 constructed-response	5 minutes
	Reading – Part 1 (Passage 2)	8 multiple choice items	15–20 minutes
		1 constructed-response	5 minutes
1–3	Reading – Part 2 (High-Frequency Words)	6 multiple-choice items	8 minutes
4–6	Reading – Part 2 (Vocabulary)	6 multiple-choice items	8 minutes
1–6	Reading – Part 3 (Phonics)	12 multiple-choice items	20–25 minutes
1–6	Reading – Part 4 (Grammar, Usage, Mechanics) OPTIONAL	6 multiple-choice items	8 minutes
1–6	Writing – Part 5 OPTIONAL	1 writing prompt	30 minutes

The End-of-Year Benchmark Test has longer passages, sixty multiple-choice items, two constructed-response items, and one writing prompt. To administer the End-of-Year Test, plan on about 2 hours for Reading — Parts 1–4 and 30 minutes for Writing — Part 5.

Directions for Administering the Tests

Before you administer a test . . .

Review the test directions below and on pages T8 through T11. Modify the directions as needed based on how you decide to administer each test. For Reading – Parts 1–4, children can mark their responses directly on their tests. In Writing – Part 5, children write compositions in response to a prompt. They write their responses on the lined page in their test booklets. You may wish to provide scrap paper that children can use to plan their writing. Only the writing in their test booklets will be scored.

When you are ready to administer a test . . .

Distribute a test to each child. Have children write their names on the front of their tests (and on any additional sheets of paper they may use). Hold up the test for children to see and have them flip through the test as you point out and explain its key features. For example, point out directions, passage titles, passages, art, Go On and Stop symbols, multiple-choice questions with answer choices, constructed-response questions with lines for written answers, and the writing prompt with a checklist and a lined page for the compositions. Allow time for children to ask any questions they may have about the test's contents before you begin the test.

Directions in **bold** type on pages T8 – T11 are intended to be read aloud. Other directions are intended for your information only. For Reading – Part 1, modify the general directions as needed if you intend to skip the constructed-response questions. For Writing – Part 5, you may wish to modify directions regarding the amount of time suggested for the testing session to match the time allowed for your state's writing test.

The Unit 1 Benchmark Test has some phonics questions in Reading – Part 3 that require additional oral instructions. These instructions follow the general directions for Reading – Parts 1 and 2.

Directions for Reading – Part 1: Comprehension (Units 1–6)

Questions 1–16

This is a test about reading and writing. In the first part, you will read two selections and answer some questions about each one. There are two types of questions: multiple-choice questions and questions that ask you to write a short answer.

Mark your answers to the multiple-choice questions in your test. For each question, circle on your answer sheet that goes with the answer you choose. Fill in the circle completely and make your mark heavy and dark. If you want to change your answer, completely erase the mark you made and fill in a different circle. Do not make any other marks in your test.

For all children, say:

For Questions A and B, write your answers on the lines in your test. Think carefully and write your ideas as clearly as you can. Allow about 5 minutes to answer each of these questions.

Read the directions carefully. You can ask me to explain any directions you do not understand. Read the selections and the questions very carefully. You may look back at a selection as often as you like to help you answer the questions.

Answer the questions you are sure about first. If a question seems too difficult, skip it and go back to it later. Check each answer to make sure it is the best answer for the question asked.

Think positively. Some questions may seem hard, but others will be easy. Relax. Most people get nervous about tests. It's natural. Just do your best.

(Depending on children's reading abilities, you may choose to read aloud directions and questions for some tests during the first part of the school year.)

Continue with Reading — Part 1: Comprehension. When you see the STOP sign at the end of Question B, put your pencils down and look up at me and wait for me to tell you what to do next. DO NOT move on after you finish Question B until I have told you to do so.

Tell children how much of the test they are expected to complete in this sitting and how much time they have to complete their work. Allow time for children to ask any questions about the directions. Then direct children to open their tests to a specified page and begin. You may wish to give the children a break upon completion of this part of the test. When the children are ready, proceed with the next activity.

Directions for Reading – Part 2: High-Frequency Words (Units 1–3)

Questions 17–22

Make sure children are on page 12. Read the directions aloud. Tell the children how much time they have to complete their work for this part. Point out the STOP sign at the end of this part, instructing them to put their pencils down and look up when they come to the STOP sign. That way you can wait for all children to complete the section before moving on to the next part.

Now turn to page 12 and read the directions. For Numbers 17 through 22, mark the word that best fits in each sentence. Fill in the bubble beside your answer. When you have finished with Number 22, put your pencils down and look up.

Directions for Reading – Part 2: Vocabulary (Units 4–6)

Questions 17–22

Make sure children are on page 12. Read the directions aloud. Tell the children how much time they have to complete their work for this part. Point out the STOP sign at the end of this part, instructing them to put their pencils down and look up when they come to the STOP sign. That way you can wait for all children to complete the section before moving on to the next part.

Now turn to page 12 and read the directions. For Numbers 17 through 22, mark the answer to each question. When you have finished with Number 22, put your pencils down and look up.

Directions for Reading – Part 3: Phonics (Unit 1)

NOTE: The Phonics Section of the Unit 1 Test is to be read aloud to children. The directions and questions are below in bold. For all other units, the children will read the questions independently. For directions to these units, read the "Directions for Reading – Part 3: Phonics (Units 2–6)" instructions on page T10.

Now I will read to you Numbers 23 through 34. After each question, fill in the circle beside your answer.

Pause after each question to allow children to mark their answers.

23. **Roy was carrying a basket and a <u>blanket</u>.**
    What word has the same beginning sounds as *blanket … blanket*?

24. **Mike wrote, "Before <u>long</u>, we flew over a big forest."**
    What word has the same ending sound as *long … long*?

25. **Roy set out milk to <u>drink</u>.**
    What word has the same ending sounds as *drink … drink*?

26. Roy put the blanket on the ground in the shade <u>beneath</u> the tree.
    What word has the same ending sound as *beneath … beneath?*

27. Roy set out <u>bread</u>, apples, cookies, and milk.
    What word rhymes with *bread … bread?*

28. Which shows the correct way to add <u>ing</u> to the word *come … come?*

29. Jack brought his toys to <u>use</u> in the sand.
    What word has the same ending sound as *use … use?*

30. In the story, the cars looked <u>like</u> toys.
    What word has the same middle sound as *like … like?*

31. Mike wrote, "All the houses and <u>streets</u> looked tiny."
    What word has the same beginning sounds as *streets … streets?*

32. On the airplane Mike sat <u>next</u> to the window.
    What word has the same middle sound as *next … next?*

33. Find the correct word to fit in this sentence.
    Mike saw many people … *what* … on the airplane.

34. Roy put the blanket on the ground in the <u>shade</u> beneath the tree.
    What word has the same beginning sound as *shade … shade?*

Directions for Reading – Part 3: Phonics (Units 2–6)

NOTE: These directions are for Units 2 through 6.
Make sure the children are on the correct page.

For Numbers 23 through 34, mark the answer to each question. Read each question carefully and then fill in the circle beside your answer. Look up when you have finished Number 34.

You may decide to give the children a break after this section. When everyone is ready, continue with the next section.

Directions for Reading – Part 4: Grammar, Usage, Mechanics (Units 1–6) OPTIONAL

For Numbers 35 through 40, find the answer to each question. Fill in the circle beside your answer. Look up when you have finished Number 40.

You may decide to give the children a break after this section. When everyone is ready, continue with the next section.

Directions for Writing – Part 5 (Units 1–6) OPTIONAL

Make sure the children are on the correct page. You may wish to give them scrap paper to use to plan their writing.

For the last part of the test, you will do a writing exercise. The writing prompt explains what you are going to write about and gives you some ideas for planning your writing. Before you begin writing, think about what you want to say and how you want to say it. You can use scrap paper to jot down your ideas.

After planning what you will write, write your response on the lined page in your test. Be sure the writing does what the prompt asks you to do. Only the writing in your test booklet will be scored.

Your writing may be about something that is real or make-believe, but remember, you are to write ONLY about the prompt in your test booklet.

You may give your writing a title if you would like, but you do not have to title your writing.

You may NOT use a dictionary. If you do not know how to spell a word, sound the word out and do the best you can.

You may either print or write in cursive. It is important to write as neatly as possible.

Make sure that your writing is easy to read. Use complete sentences and choose your words carefully.

I cannot read the prompt to you or help you plan what to write. You must read the prompt and plan your writing on your own. Remember, read the prompt carefully and then plan your writing. (Depending on a child's reading ability, you may wish to omit these directions and read the writing prompt aloud for some or all of the tests.)

You have a total of 30 minutes to read, plan, and respond to the prompt. I will let you know when you have 5 minutes left. (You may wish to modify the amount of time you allow for the Writing – Part 5 section to match children's needs or to match the time allowed on your state's writing tests.)

If you finish early, please review your writing in your test. Use the questions in the "Checklist for Writers" to help you check and edit your writing.

Allow time for children to ask any questions about the directions. Then, direct children to open their tests to the writing prompt page, read the prompt, plan their writing, and then write their compositions. Be sure to alert children when they have 5 minutes left.

Directions for scoring the tests begin below. Answer keys begin on page T40. Evaluation Charts (T25–T38) are provided along with a class record chart on page T39.

SCORING THE TESTS

The Benchmark Tests are intended to be scored by part–a total score for Reading – Parts 1–4 and a separate score for Writing – Part 5. To make scoring easier, copy and use the following charts as needed:

- the Unit Benchmark Evaluation Charts, beginning on page T25, for recording a child's individual scores on a Unit Benchmark Test;

- the End-of-Year Benchmark Test Evaluation Chart, on pages T37 and T38, for recording a child's individual scores on the End-of-Year Benchmark Test;

- the Class Record Chart, on page T39, for recording test scores for all children for all six units.

Answer keys for each test begin on page T40. In Reading – Part 1, there are two types of items: multiple-choice questions and constructed-response questions. These types of items are scored in slightly different ways, as explained below. In Writing – Part 5, each prompt is linked to one of four different types of writing: narrative, descriptive, expository, or persuasive. For each type of writing, there are four Writing Scoring Rubrics. Each rubric has a different point scale. Choose the rubric that most closely matches the rubric for your state's writing tests or the rubric you deem most appropriate for your children. Writing Scoring Rubrics begin on page T14.

Scoring Multiple-Choice Questions

Each multiple-choice question has three answer choices. The answer keys list the complete response to each question. Refer to the answer key for the test you are scoring and mark each multiple-choice question correct (1 point) or incorrect (0 points).

Scoring Constructed-Response Questions

Use the answer keys beginning on page T40 and the rubric on the next page to help you score constructed-response questions. Award each constructed-response answer a score from 0 to 2 points, depending on how accurate and complete the response is. The answer keys provide abbreviated descriptions of top responses. Have an ideal top response in your mind before you assess children's responses.

Constructed-Response Scoring Rubric

Points	Description
2	The response indicates a **full understanding** of the question's reading or critical thinking skill. The response is accurate and complete. Necessary support and/or examples are included, and the information is clearly text-based.
1	The response indicates a **partial understanding** of the question's reading or critical thinking skill. The response includes information that is essentially correct and text-based, but it is too general or too simplistic. Some of the support and/or examples may be incomplete or omitted.
0	The response is **inaccurate**, confused, and/or irrelevant, or the child has failed to respond to the task.

Scoring the Writing Component (Part 5)

To evaluate children's responses to a writing prompt, familiarize yourself with the writing prompt and review the Writing Scoring Rubrics on pages T14–T21. Identify the type of writing suggested in the writing prompt. (Types of writing for each prompt are identified in the answer keys that begin on page T40.) Then choose one of the four Writing Scoring Rubrics provided for that type of writing. Use the rubric to score each composition on a scale from 1 to 6, 1 to 5, 1 to 4, or 1 to 3.

Writing Scoring Rubrics: Narrative Writing

6-Point Scoring Rubric

6	5	4	3	2	1
• narrative writing is well focused on the topic • contains clear ideas • logically organized; uses transitions • voice is engaging; well suited to purpose and audience • demonstrates varied, precise word choice • sentences are fluent and varied • shows excellent control of writing conventions	• narrative writing is focused on the topic • most ideas are clear • logically organized; uses some transitions • voice comes through well; suited to purpose and audience • generally demonstrates varied, precise word choice • most sentences are complete and varied • shows very good control of writing conventions	• narrative writing is generally focused on the topic • ideas are generally clear • logically organized with some lapses; has transitions • voice comes through occasionally; suited to purpose and audience • often demonstrates varied, precise word choice • many sentences are complete and varied • shows good control of writing conventions	• narrative writing is generally focused but may stray from the topic • ideas may be somewhat unclear • somewhat organized; may lack transitions • voice uneven; not always suited to purpose or audience • word choice could be more varied, precise • some incomplete sentences; little variety • shows fair control of writing conventions	• narrative writing is minimally related to the topic • ideas are often unclear • minimally organized; no transitions • slight evidence of voice; little sense of purpose or audience • poor choice of words; limited vocabulary • sentences are incomplete; show little or no variety • shows little knowledge of writing conventions	• narrative writing is not focused on the topic • ideas are unclear • unorganized; no transitions • weak voice; no sense of purpose or audience • limited vocabulary • gross errors in sentence structure • shows no knowledge of writing conventions

5-Point Scoring Rubric

5	4	3	2	1
• narrative writing is well focused on the topic • contains clear ideas • logically organized; uses transitions • voice is engaging; well suited to purpose and audience • demonstrates varied, precise word choice • sentences are complete and varied • shows excellent control of writing conventions	• narrative writing is focused on the topic • most ideas are clear • logically organized; uses some transitions • voice is fairly strong; suited to purpose and audience • generally demonstrates varied, precise word choice • most sentences are complete and varied • shows very good control of writing conventions	• narrative writing is generally focused on the topic • ideas are generally clear • logically organized with some lapses; transitions weak • voice comes through occasionally; may not suit purpose or audience • word choice could be more varied, precise • many sentences are complete; generally varied • shows fairly good control of writing conventions	• narrative writing strays from the topic • many ideas are unclear • little organization; few or no transitions • voice comes through rarely; poorly suited to purpose or audience • choice of words limited • incomplete sentences; little variety • shows frequent errors in writing conventions	• narrative writing is not focused on the topic • ideas are unclear • unorganized; no transitions • weak voice; no sense of audience or purpose • choice of words very limited • incomplete sentences; no variety • shows many serious errors in writing conventions

Writing Scoring Rubrics: Narrative Writing

4-Point Scoring Rubric

4	3	2	1
• narrative writing is well focused on the topic • contains clear ideas • logically organized; uses transitions • voice is engaging; well suited to purpose and audience • demonstrates varied, precise word choice • sentences are complete and varied • shows excellent control of writing conventions	• narrative writing is focused on the topic • most ideas are clear • logically organized; uses some transitions • voice is fairly strong; suited to purpose and audience • generally demonstrates varied, precise word choice • most sentences are complete and varied • shows very good control of writing conventions	• narrative writing may stray from the topic • ideas may be unclear • little organization; may be few or no transitions • slight evidence of voice; may be poorly suited to purpose or audience • choice of words limited • incomplete sentences present; little variety • shows frequent errors in writing conventions	• narrative writing is not focused on the topic • ideas are unclear • unorganized; no transitions • weak voice; no sense of audience or purpose • choice of words very limited • incomplete sentences; no variety • shows many serious errors in writing conventions

3-Point Scoring Rubric

3	2	1
• narrative writing is well focused on the topic • contains clear ideas • logically organized; uses transitions • voice is engaging; well suited to purpose and audience • demonstrates varied, precise word choice • sentences are complete and varied • shows excellent control of writing conventions	• narrative writing is generally focused on the topic • ideas are sometimes unclear • logically organized with lapses; transitions need improvement • voice comes through fairly well; may not suit purpose or audience • word choice could be more varied, precise • some sentences are complete and varied • shows frequent errors in writing conventions	• narrative writing is not focused on the topic • ideas are unclear • unorganized; no transitions • weak voice; no sense of audience • choice of words very limited • incomplete sentences; no variety • shows little or no control of writing conventions

© Pearson Education 2

Writing Scoring Rubrics: Descriptive Writing

6-Point Scoring Rubric

6	5	4	3	2	1
• descriptive writing is well focused on the topic • contains clear ideas • logically organized; uses transitions • voice is engaging; well suited to purpose and audience • precise, vivid language paints strong pictures • sentences are fluent and varied • shows excellent control of writing conventions	• descriptive writing is focused on the topic • most ideas are clear • logically organized; uses some transitions • voice comes through well; suited to purpose and audience • generally demonstrates varied, precise word choice • most sentences are complete and varied • shows very good control of writing conventions	• descriptive writing is generally focused on the topic • ideas are generally clear • logically organized with some lapses; has transitions • voice comes through occasionally; suited to purpose and audience • often demonstrates varied, precise word choice • many sentences are complete and varied • shows good control of writing conventions	• descriptive writing may stray from the topic • ideas may be somewhat unclear • somewhat organized; may lack transitions • voice uneven; not always suited to purpose or audience • word choice could be more varied, precise • some incomplete sentences; little variety • shows frequent errors in writing conventions	• descriptive writing is minimally related to the topic • ideas are often unclear • minimally organized; no transitions • slight evidence of voice; little sense of purpose or audience • poor choice of words; limited vocabulary • sentences are incomplete; show little or no variety • shows little knowledge of writing conventions	• descriptive writing is not focused on the topic • ideas are unclear • unorganized; no transitions • weak voice; no sense of purpose or audience • limited vocabulary • gross errors in sentence structure • shows no knowledge of writing conventions

5-Point Scoring Rubric

5	4	3	2	1
• descriptive writing is well focused on the topic • contains clear ideas • logically organized; uses transitions • voice is engaging; well suited to purpose and audience • demonstrates varied, precise word choice • sentences are complete and varied • shows excellent control of writing conventions	• descriptive writing is focused on the topic • most ideas are clear • logically organized; uses some transitions • voice is fairly engaging; suited to purpose and audience • generally demonstrates varied, precise word choice • most sentences are complete and varied • shows very good control of writing conventions	• descriptive writing is generally focused on the topic • ideas are generally clear • logically organized with some lapses; transitions somewhat weak • voice comes through occasionally; may not suit purpose or audience • word choice could be more varied, precise • many sentences are complete; generally varied • shows fairly good control of writing conventions	• descriptive writing strays from the topic • many ideas are unclear • little organization; few or no transitions • voice comes through rarely; poorly suited to purpose or audience • word choice limited • incomplete sentences; little variety • shows frequent errors in writing conventions	• descriptive writing is not focused on the topic • ideas are unclear • unorganized; no transitions • weak voice; no sense of audience or purpose • word choice very limited • incomplete sentences; no variety • shows many serious errors in writing conventions

Writing Scoring Rubrics: Descriptive Writing

4-Point Scoring Rubric

4	3	2	1
• descriptive writing is well focused on the topic	• descriptive writing is focused on the topic	• descriptive writing may stray from the topic	• descriptive writing is not focused on the topic
• contains clear ideas	• most ideas are clear	• ideas may be somewhat unclear	• ideas are unclear
• logically organized; uses transitions	• logically organized; uses some transitions	• little organization with some lapses; transitions somewhat weak	• unorganized; no transitions
• voice is engaging; well suited to purpose and audience	• voice is fairly engaging; suited to purpose and audience	• slight evidence of voice; may be poorly suited to audience or purpose	• weak voice; no sense of audience or purpose
• demonstrates varied, precise word choice	• generally demonstrates varied, precise word choice	• choice of words limited	• word choice very limited
• sentences are complete and varied	• most sentences are complete and varied	• incomplete sentences present; little variety	• incomplete sentences; no variety
• shows excellent control of writing conventions	• shows very good control of writing conventions	• shows frequent errors in writing conventions	• shows many serious errors in writing conventions

3-Point Scoring Rubric

3	2	1
• descriptive writing is well focused on the topic	• descriptive writing is generally focused on the topic	• descriptive writing is not focused on the topic
• contains clear ideas	• ideas are sometimes unclear	• ideas are unclear
• logically organized; uses transitions	• logically organized with lapses; transitions need improvement	• unorganized; no transitions
• voice is engaging; well suited to purpose and audience	• voice comes through fairly well; may not suit purpose or audience	• weak voice; no sense of purpose or audience
• demonstrates varied, precise word choice	• word choice could be more varied, precise	• choice of words very limited
• sentences are complete and varied	• some sentences are complete and varied	• incomplete sentences; no variety
• shows excellent control of writing conventions	• shows frequent errors in writing conventions	• shows little or no control of writing conventions

Writing Scoring Rubrics: Descriptive Writing

Writing Scoring Rubrics: Expository Writing

6-Point Scoring Rubric

6	5	4	3	2	1
• expository writing is well focused on the topic • contains clear ideas • logically organized; uses transitions • voice is engaging; well suited to purpose and audience • demonstrates varied, precise word choice • sentences are complete and varied • shows excellent control of writing conventions	• expository writing is focused on the topic • most ideas are clear • logically organized; uses some transitions • voice comes through well; suited to purpose and audience • generally demonstrates varied, precise word choice • most sentences are complete and varied • shows very good control of writing conventions	• expository writing is generally focused on the topic • ideas are generally clear • logically organized with some lapses; has transitions • voice comes through occasionally; suited to purpose and audience • often demonstrates varied, precise word choice • many sentences are complete and varied • shows good control of writing conventions	• expository writing may stray from the topic • ideas may be somewhat unclear • little organization; few or no transitions • voice uneven; not always suited to purpose or audience • word choice could be more varied, precise • some incomplete sentences; little variety • shows frequent errors in writing conventions	• expository writing is minimally related to the topic • ideas are often unclear • minimally organized; no transitions • slight evidence of voice; little sense of purpose or audience • poor choice of words; limited vocabulary • sentences are incomplete; show little or no variety • shows many serious errors in writing conventions	• expository writing is not focused on the topic • ideas are unclear • unorganized; no transitions • weak voice; no sense of purpose or audience • limited vocabulary • gross errors in sentence structure • shows no knowledge of writing conventions

5-Point Scoring Rubric

5	4	3	2	1
• expository writing is well focused on the topic • contains clear ideas • logically organized; uses transitions • voice is engaging; well suited to purpose and audience • demonstrates varied, precise word choice • sentences are complete and varied • shows excellent control of writing conventions	• expository writing is focused on the topic • most ideas are clear • logically organized; uses some transitions • voice is fairly engaging; suited to purpose and audience • generally demonstrates varied, precise word choice • most sentences are complete and varied • shows very good control of writing conventions	• expository writing is generally focused on the topic • ideas are generally clear • logically organized with some lapses; transitions somewhat weak • voice comes through occasionally; may not suit purpose or audience • word choice could be more varied, precise • many sentences are complete; generally varied • shows fairly good control of writing conventions	• expository writing strays from the topic • many ideas are unclear • little organization; few or no transitions • voice comes through rarely; poorly suited to purpose or audience • word choice limited • incomplete sentences; little variety • shows frequent errors in writing conventions	• expository writing is not focused on the topic • ideas are unclear • unorganized; no transitions • weak voice; no sense of audience or purpose • word choice very limited • incomplete sentences; no variety • shows many serious errors in writing conventions

Writing Scoring Rubrics: Expository Writing

Benchmark Test Teacher's Manual

Writing Scoring Rubrics: Expository Writing

4-Point Scoring Rubric

4	3	2	1
• expository writing is well focused on the topic • contains clear ideas • logically organized; uses transitions • voice is engaging; well suited to purpose and audience • demonstrates varied, precise word choice • sentences are complete and varied • shows excellent control of writing conventions	• expository writing is focused on the topic • most ideas are clear • logically organized; uses some transitions • voice is fairly engaging; suited to purpose and audience • generally demonstrates varied, precise word choice • most sentences are complete and varied • shows very good control of writing conventions	• expository writing may stray from the topic • ideas may be somewhat unclear • logically organized with some lapses; may be few or no transitions • slight evidence of voice; may be poorly suited to audience or purpose • choice of words limited • incomplete sentences present; little variety • shows frequent errors in writing conventions	• expository writing is not focused on the topic • ideas are unclear • unorganized; no transitions • weak voice; no sense of audience or purpose • word choice very limited • incomplete sentences; no variety • shows many serious errors in writing conventions

3-Point Scoring Rubric

3	2	1
• expository writing is well focused on the topic • contains clear ideas • logically organized; uses transitions • voice is engaging; well suited to purpose and audience • demonstrates varied, precise word choice • sentences are complete and varied • shows excellent control of writing conventions	• expository writing is generally focused on the topic • ideas are sometimes unclear • logically organized with lapses; transitions need improvement • voice comes through fairly well; may not suit purpose or audience • word choice could be more varied, precise • some sentences are complete and varied • shows frequent errors in writing conventions	• expository writing is not focused on the topic • ideas are unclear • unorganized; no transitions • weak voice; no sense of purpose or audience • choice of words very limited • incomplete sentences; no variety • shows little or no control of writing conventions

Writing Scoring Rubrics: Persuasive Writing

6-Point Scoring Rubric

6	5	4	3	2	1
• persuasive writing is well focused on the topic • contains clear ideas • logically organized; presents reasons in order • voice is engaging; well suited to purpose and audience • demonstrates precise, persuasive wording • sentences are fluent and varied • shows excellent control of writing conventions	• persuasive writing is focused on the topic • most ideas are clear • logically organized; presents reasons in some order • voice comes through well; suited to purpose and audience • generally demonstrates precise, persuasive word choice • most sentences are complete and varied • shows very good control of writing conventions	• persuasive writing is generally focused on the topic • ideas are generally clear • logically organized with some lapses; presents most reasons in order • voice comes through occasionally; suited to purpose and audience • often demonstrates precise, persuasive word choice • many sentences are complete and varied • shows good control of writing conventions	• persuasive writing is generally focused but may stray from the topic • ideas may be somewhat unclear • somewhat organized; reasons may not be in proper order • voice uneven; not always suited to purpose or audience • word choice is not always precise or persuasive • some incomplete sentences; little variety • shows fair control of writing conventions	• persuasive writing is minimally related to the topic • ideas are often unclear • minimally organized; reasons are not in order • slight evidence of voice; little sense of audience or purpose • poor choice of words; not very persuasive • sentences are incomplete; show little or no variety • shows little knowledge of writing conventions	• persuasive writing is not focused on the topic • ideas are unclear • unorganized; reasons, if any, are not in order • weak voice; no sense of purpose or audience • limited vocabulary; fails to persuade • gross errors in sentence structure • shows no knowledge of writing conventions

5-Point Scoring Rubric

5	4	3	2	1
• persuasive writing is well focused on the topic • contains clear ideas • logically organized; presents reasons in order • voice is engaging; well suited to purpose and audience • demonstrates precise, persuasive wording • sentences are complete and varied • shows excellent control of writing conventions	• persuasive writing is focused on the topic • most ideas are clear • logically organized; presents reasons in some order • voice is fairly engaging; suited to purpose and audience • generally demonstrates precise, persuasive word choice • most sentences are complete and varied • shows very good control of writing conventions	• persuasive writing is generally focused on the topic • ideas are generally clear • logically organized with some lapses; presents most reasons in order • voice comes through occasionally; may not suit purpose or audience • word choice could be more precise, persuasive • many sentences are complete; generally varied • shows fairly good control of writing conventions	• persuasive writing strays from the topic • many ideas are unclear • little organization; reasons are not in order • voice comes through rarely; poorly suited to audience or purpose • word choice limited; not persuasive • incomplete sentences; little variety • shows frequent errors in writing conventions	• persuasive writing is not focused on the topic • ideas are unclear • unorganized; reasons, if any, are not in order • weak voice; no sense of audience or purpose • word choice very limited; fails to persuade • incomplete sentences; no variety • shows many serious errors in writing conventions

Writing Scoring Rubrics: Persuasive Writing

4-Point Scoring Rubric

4	3	2	1
• persuasive writing is well focused on the topic • contains clear ideas • logically organized; presents reasons in order • voice is engaging; well suited to purpose and audience • demonstrates precise, persuasive wording • sentences are complete and varied • shows excellent control of writing conventions	• persuasive writing is focused on the topic • most ideas are clear • logically organized; presents reasons in some order • voice is fairly engaging; suited to purpose and audience • generally demonstrates precise, persuasive word choice • most sentences are complete and varied • shows very good control of writing conventions	• persuasive writing may stray from the topic • ideas may be somewhat unclear • logically organized with some lapses; reasons may not be in order • slight evidence of voice; may be poorly suited to purpose or audience • choice of words limited; not very persuasive • incomplete sentences present; little variety • shows frequent errors in writing conventions	• persuasive writing is not focused on the topic • ideas are unclear • unorganized; reasons, if any, are not in order • weak voice; no sense of audience or purpose • word choice very limited; fails to persuade • incomplete sentences; no variety • shows many serious errors in writing conventions

3-Point Scoring Rubric

3	2	1
• persuasive writing is well focused on the topic • contains clear ideas • logically organized; presents reasons in order • voice is engaging; well suited to purpose and audience • demonstrates precise, persuasive word choice • sentences are complete and varied • shows excellent control of writing conventions	• persuasive writing is generally focused on the topic • ideas are sometimes unclear • logically organized with lapses; presents most reasons in order • voice comes through fairly well; may not suit audience or purpose • word choice could be more precise, persuasive • some sentences are complete and varied • shows frequent errors in writing conventions	• persuasive writing is not focused on the topic • ideas are unclear • unorganized; reasons, if any, are not in order • weak voice; no sense of audience or purpose • choice of words very limited; fails to persuade • incomplete sentences; no variety • shows little or no control of writing conventions

Writing Scoring Rubrics: Persuasive Writing

Using an Evaluation Chart

Use the Evaluation Charts on pages T25 through T38 to score the Unit Benchmark Tests and the End-of-Year Benchmark Test. To score one of these tests using an Evaluation Chart, use the following procedure:

1. Make a copy of the appropriate Evaluation Chart for each child.

2. To score Reading – Parts 1–4, circle the score for each item on the Evaluation Chart. Multiple-choice questions are scored 0 or 1 point (incorrect or correct). Constructed-response questions are scored 0, 1, or 2 points, depending on how accurate and complete the response is. Use the answer key for the test you are scoring and the Constructed-Response Scoring Rubric on page T13 to help you score Parts 1–4.

3. Find the child's total score for Reading – Parts 1–4 by adding the individual scores for all items.

4. Use the formula on the Evaluation Chart to find the percentage score for Reading (Parts 1–4) by dividing the total *obtained* score by the total *possible* score and then multiplying the quotient by 100.

5. To score Writing – Part 5, identify the type of writing suggested in the prompt and choose one of the four Writing Scoring Rubrics for that type of writing. Read the child's writing and score each composition on a scale from 1 to 6, 1 to 5, 1 to 4, or 1 to 3.

6. Mark the child's Writing score on the Evaluation Chart. Add any notes or observations about the writing that may be helpful to you and the child in later instruction.

INTERPRETING TEST RESULTS

A child's score on a Benchmark Test provides only one look at the child's progress and should be interpreted in conjunction with other assessments and the teacher's observations. However, a low score on one or both parts of a Benchmark Test probably indicates a need for closer review of the child's performance and perhaps additional instruction.

Regrouping for Instruction

The Benchmark Tests can help you make regrouping decisions. In Grade 2 there are opportunities for regrouping at the end of Unit 2, 3, 4, and 5. Depending on each child's progress, teachers may prefer to regroup more or less frequently.

Children who score below 60% on the multiple-choice items of the Comprehension, Vocabulary, and Phonics sections of the Benchmark Tests and who meet other criteria supplied on the *Assess and Regroup* pages at the back of each Teacher's Edition would benefit from being in the Strategic Intervention group for the next unit of instruction.

Children who score between 60% and 79% on the multiple-choice items of the Comprehension, Vocabulary, and Phonics sections of the Benchmark Tests likely belong in the On-Level reading group, but you will want to consider performance on the Day 5 Assessments, fluency scores, and all other criteria supplied on the *Assess and Regroup* pages at the back of each Teacher's Edition.

Children who score 80% to 94% on the multiple-choice items of the Comprehension, Vocabulary, and Phonics sections of the Benchmark Tests and who meet other criteria supplied on the Assess and Regroup pages at the back of each Teacher's Edition are capable of continuing in or moving into the On-Level reading group for the next unit of instruction.

Children who score 95% or greater on the multiple-choice items of the Comprehension, Vocabulary, and Phonics sections of the Benchmark Tests and who meet other criteria supplied on the *Assess and Regroup* pages at the back of each Teacher's Edition may be capable of work in the Advanced reading group for the next unit of instruction.

Further Analysis of Results

Each Reading (Parts 1–4) item on an Evaluation Chart is linked to a tested skill. By identifying which items the child answered incorrectly and referring to the list of tested skills, you may be able to determine specific skills or areas in which the child needs additional help. For example, if the child answers six questions incorrectly and several involve literary elements such as plot and character, you may want to plan additional instruction for the child in this area. While the Benchmark Tests do not provide sufficient content coverage of individual skills to be truly "diagnostic," children's performance patterns can often provide useful clues as to particular strengths and weaknesses.

Grading: For more information on how to use a writing assessment scale as an element of classroom grades, refer to the "Grading Writing" section of the *Assessment Handbook*.

Measuring the Progress of English Language Learners

Children whose native language is not English present unique challenges to educators as they administer and score formal assessments, interpret scores, and make decisions based on test scores. Although many English language learners quickly master *social* English, the conversational language skills and conventions used in everyday interactions with classmates, they frequently encounter difficulty with the *academic* English found on formal assessments. The performance of these children is greatly affected by:

- the increasing linguistic demands of vocabulary, including specialized terms, multiple-meaning words, and abstract concepts; and

- structural analysis constraints at the word, sentence, paragraph, and text levels.

There are a number of ways to accommodate the needs of English language learners to ensure fairness and full participation in the *Scott Foresman Reading Street* formal assessments. A general rule of thumb is to use the same accommodations in testing situations as used in instruction. For instance, if children receive part of their instruction in their home language, then it is appropriate to translate test directions and comprehension questions into that language. Acceptable accommodations might include:

- providing additional testing time and allowing frequent or extended breaks;

- administering the tests at times most beneficial to the children;

- administering the tests in small groups or in one-on-one settings;

- reading test directions to children in English or in the children's home languages, and repeating as needed;

- simplifying the language and sentence structure of test directions;

- requesting that children restate and clarify test directions in their own words;

- discussing the pictures and any graphics, such as maps, to ensure that children can interpret them;

- allowing the use of bilingual dictionaries;

- reading comprehension questions orally to children in English or in their home languages; and

- allowing children to respond orally to questions or dictate answers for transcription.

In providing accommodations to children, it is important not to compromise the intent of the assessment. Keep these points in mind:

- Do not read the comprehension passages aloud to children or translate them into children's home languages.

- When assessing English vocabulary and grammar skills, do not translate test items into the home language.

- When assessing children's writing ability in English, do not transcribe their oral responses to the writing prompts.

These practices would alter the constructs of the assessments. For example, the reading comprehension assessments are designed to measure both word recognition and understanding, so reading the selections to children would actually change the intent of the test.

Following the administration of the formal assessments, it is important to note which accommodations were used for the English language learners and to interpret scores with that information in mind.

Informal assessments play an important role in accurately measuring the progress of English language learners. For more information on assessment and English language learners, see the *ELL and Transition Handbook,* as well as Chapter 4 of the *Assessment Handbook.*

Evaluation Chart: Grade 2 – Unit 1 Benchmark Test

Student Name _____ **Date** _____

Reading – Parts 1–4			
Item	**Tested Skill**	**Item Type***	**Score** (circle one)
Reading – Part 1: Comprehension			
1.	Literary Elements: Setting	L	0 1
2.	Main Idea and Details	I	0 1
3.	Realism and Fantasy	C	0 1
4.	Synonyms	I	0 1
5.	Main Idea and Details	C	0 1
6.	Main Idea and Details	I	0 1
7.	Literary Elements: Character	I	0 1
8.	Main Idea and Details	C	0 1
A.	Constructed-Response Text-to-Self Connection		0 1 2
9.	Literary Elements: Setting	I	0 1
10.	Main Idea and Details	L	0 1
11.	Literary Elements: Character	I	0 1
12.	Literary Elements: Setting	C	0 1
13.	Main Idea and Details	I	0 1
14.	Author's Purpose	C	0 1
15.	Literary Elements: Character	I	0 1
16.	Literary Elements: Character	I	0 1
B.	Constructed-Response Text-to-Text Connection		0 1 2
Reading – Part 2: High-Frequency Words			
17.	High-Frequency Words		0 1
18.	High-Frequency Words		0 1
19.	High-Frequency Words		0 1
20.	High-Frequency Words		0 1
21.	High-Frequency Words		0 1
22.	High-Frequency Words		0 1
Reading – Part 3: Phonics			
23.	Consonant Blends: 2-letter initial; digraph *th*		0 1
24.	Consonant Digraph: *ng; g/j/*		0 1
25.	Consonant Blends: 2-letter ending, *nk*		0 1
26.	Consonant Digraphs: *th, tch*		0 1
27.	Short *e: ea*		0 1
28.	Base Words/Ending -*ing* with spelling change		0 1

■ ▬ **E v a l u a t i o n   C h a r t :   G r a d e   2 – U n i t   1   B e n c h m a r k   T e s t** ▬ ■

Reading – Part 3: Phonics (continued)			
29.	*s*/z/, *c*/s/	0	1
30.	Long Vowel: CVCe	0	1
31.	Consonant Blends: 3-letter blends	0	1
32.	Short Vowels: CVC, CVCC, CCVC	0	1
33.	Base Words/Ending *-ing* with spelling change	0	1
34.	Consonant Digraphs: *sh, ch*	0	1
Student's Regrouping Multiple-Choice Score/Total Possible Score		_____/34	
Reading – Part 4: Grammar, Usage, Mechanics			
35.	Sentences	0	1
36.	Sentences	0	1
37.	Sentences	0	1
38.	Sentences	0	1
39.	Sentences	0	1
40.	Sentences	0	1
Student's Reading Total Score/Total Possible Score		_____/44	

*L = literal   I = inferential   C = critical analysis

Regrouping (Reading – Parts 1–3) percentage: _____ ÷ 34 = _____ × 100 = _____%

      (student's score)   (percentage score)

Reading – Parts 1–4 percentage score: _____ ÷ 44 = _____ × 100 = _____%

      (student's total score)   (percentage score)

Writing – Part 5

Writing Score (Complete one.) _____/6 _____/5 _____/4 _____/3

Notes/Observations:

Evaluation Chart: Grade 2 – Unit 2 Benchmark Test

Student Name _____ Date _____

Item	Tested Skill	Item Type*	Score (circle one)
Reading – Parts 1–4			
Reading – Part 1: Comprehension			
1.	Literary Elements: Setting	I	0 1
2.	Sequence	L	0 1
3.	Draw Conclusions	I	0 1
4.	Sequence	I	0 1
5.	Realism/Fantasy	C	0 1
6.	Literary Elements: Character	I	0 1
7.	Draw Conclusions	C	0 1
8.	Author's Purpose	C	0 1
A.	Constructed-Response Text-to-Self Connection		0 1 2
9.	Sequence	L	0 1
10.	Sequence	L	0 1
11.	Realism/Fantasy	I	0 1
12.	Literary Elements: Character	I	0 1
13.	Sequence	I	0 1
14.	Realism/Fantasy	I	0 1
15.	Author's Purpose	I	0 1
16.	Realism/Fantasy	C	0 1
B.	Constructed-Response Text-to-Text Connection		0 1 2
Reading – Part 2: High-Frequency Words			
17.	High-Frequency Word		0 1
18.	High-Frequency Word		0 1
19.	High-Frequency Word		0 1
20.	High-Frequency Word		0 1
21.	High-Frequency Word		0 1
22.	High-Frequency Word		0 1
Reading – Part 3: Phonics			
23.	Long *a: ay*		0 1
24.	Plural *-ies* (change y to i)		0 1
25.	r-Controlled *ir*		0 1
26.	Contractions: *'ll*		0 1
27.	r-Controlled *or*		0 1
28.	Plural *-es*		0 1

© Pearson Education 2

- - - - - - **E v a l u a t i o n   C h a r t :   G r a d e   2 – U n i t   2   B e n c h m a r k   T e s t** - - - - - -

Reading – Part 3: Phonics (continued)			
29.	Contraction *'m*	0	1
30.	Long *a: ai*	0	1
31.	Contraction *n't*	0	1
32.	r-Controlled *ore*	0	1
33.	r-Controlled *ar:* syllables VCCV	0	1
34.	Contraction *'s*	0	1
Student's Regrouping Multiple-Choice Score/Total Possible Score _____**/34**			
Reading – Part 4: Grammar, Usage, Mechanics			
35.	Nouns	0	1
36.	Nouns	0	1
37.	Nouns	0	1
38.	Nouns	0	1
39.	Possessive Nouns	0	1
40.	Possessive Nouns	0	1
Student's Reading Total Score/Total Possible Score _____**/44**			

*L = literal   I = inferential   C = critical analysis

Regrouping (Reading – Parts 1–3) percentage: _____ ÷ 34 = _____ × 100 = _____%
　　　　　　　　　　　　　　　　(student's score)　　　　　　　　　　　　(percentage score)

Reading – Parts 1–4 percentage score: _____ ÷ 44 = _____ × 100 = _____%
　　　　　　　　　　　　　　(student's total score)　　　　　　　　　(percentage score)

Writing – Part 5

Writing Score (Complete one.)　_____/6　　_____/5　　_____/4　　_____/3

Notes/Observations:

Evaluation Chart: Grade 2 – Unit 3 Benchmark Test

Student Name _____ **Date** _____

Item	Tested Skill	Item Type*	Score (circle one)
Reading – Parts 1–4			
Reading – Part 1: Comprehension			
1.	Cause and Effect	I	0 1
2.	Cause and Effect	I	0 1
3.	Realism / Fantasy	C	0 1
4.	Cause and Effect	I	0 1
5.	Draw Conclusions	I	0 1
6.	Draw Conclusions	I	0 1
7.	Draw Conclusions	I	0 1
8.	Literary Elements: Plot	C	0 1
A.	Constructed-Response Text-to-Self Connection		0 1 2
9.	Main Idea and Details	C	0 1
10.	Draw Conclusions	C	0 1
11.	Draw Conclusions	I	0 1
12.	Main Idea and Details	I	0 1
13.	Sequence	I	0 1
14.	Sequence	L	0 1
15.	Vocabulary: Antonyms	I	0 1
16.	Author's Purpose	C	0 1
B.	Constructed-Response Text-to-Text Connection		0 1 2
Reading – Part 2: High-Frequency Words			
17.	High-Frequency Words		0 1
18.	High-Frequency Words		0 1
19.	High-Frequency Words		0 1
20.	High-Frequency Words		0 1
21.	High-Frequency Words		0 1
22.	High-Frequency Words		0 1
Reading – Part 3: Phonics			
23.	Long *i: ie*		0 1
24.	Comparative Ending *er*		0 1
25.	Compound Words		0 1
26.	Long *e: y*		0 1
27.	Comparative Ending *est*		0 1
28.	Long *e: ee*		0 1

Reading – Part 3: Phonics (continued)			
29.	Long *i: i* in iCC	0	1
30.	Long *o: o* in oCC; Syllables VCV (open)	0	1
31.	Long *e: ea*	0	1
32.	Long *o: ow*	0	1
33.	Compound Words	0	1
34.	Long *i: y*	0	1
Student's Regrouping Multiple-Choice Score/Total Possible Score _____ **/34**			
Reading – Part 4: Grammar, Usage, Mechanics			
35.	Verbs	0	1
36.	Verbs	0	1
37.	Verbs	0	1
38.	Verbs	0	1
39.	Verbs	0	1
40.	Verbs	0	1
Student's Reading Total Score/Total Possible Score _____ **/44**			

*L = literal   I = inferential   C = critical analysis

Regrouping (Reading – Parts 1–3) percentage: _____ ÷ 34 = _____ × 100 = _____%
                                          (student's score)   (percentage score)

Reading – Parts 1–4 percentage score: _____ ÷ 44 = _____ × 100 = _____%
                                    (student's total score)   (percentage score)

Writing – Part 5

Writing Score (Complete one.) _____/6 _____/5 _____/4 _____/3

Notes/Observations:

© Pearson Education 2

Evaluation Chart: Grade 2 – Unit 4 Benchmark Test

Student Name _____ Date _____

	Reading – Parts 1–4		
Item	**Tested Skill**	**Item Type***	**Score** (circle one)
Reading – Part 1: Comprehension			
1.	Compare and Contrast	L	0 1
2.	Compare and Contrast	I	0 1
3.	Fact and Opinion	I	0 1
4.	Fact and Opinion	I	0 1
5.	Main Idea	I	0 1
6.	Fact and Opinion	I	0 1
7.	Genre (Nonfiction)	C	0 1
8.	Fact and Opinion	I	0 1
A.	Constructed-Response Text-to-Self Connection		0 1 2
9.	Literary Elements: Plot	L	0 1
10.	Literary Elements: Character	I	0 1
11.	Literary Elements: Setting	L	0 1
12.	Literary Elements: Theme	C	0 1
13.	Literary Elements: Plot	I	0 1
14.	Draw Conclusions	C	0 1
15.	Compare and Contrast	I	0 1
16.	Compare and Contrast	I	0 1
B.	Constructed-Response Text-to-Text Connection		0 1
Reading – Part 2: Vocabulary			
17.	Context Clues: Multiple-Meaning Words		0 1
18.	Word Structures: Suffix -ful		0 1
19.	Word Structures: Prefix un-		0 1
20.	Word Structures: Suffix -ful		0 1
21.	Context Clues: Multiple-Meaning Words		0 1
22.	Context Clues: Multiple-Meaning Words		0 1
Reading – Part 3: Phonics			
23.	Syllables: Consonant + le		0 1
24.	Vowel oo (short /oo/)		0 1
25.	Vowel Diphthong ou, ow /ou/		0 1
26.	Vowel Diphthong oi, oy /oi/		0 1
27.	Vowel Pattern oo (long /oo/)		0 1
28.	Vowel Pattern ew, ue (long /oo/)		0 1

∎ ▪ ▪ ▪ ▪ Evaluation Chart: Grade 2 – Unit 4 Benchmark Test ▪ ▪ ▪ ▪ ▪ ▪ ▪ ▪ ▪ ▪ ▪ ∎

Reading – Part 3: Phonics (continued)		
29.	Vowel Diphthong *ou, ow* /ou/	0 1
30.	Vowel Pattern *ew, oo* (long /oo/)	0 1
31.	Vowel *u* as in *put*	0 1
32.	Syllables: Consonant + *le*	0 1
33.	Vowel Diphthong *ou* /ou/	0 1
34.	Vowel *oo* (short /oo/)	0 1
Student's Regrouping Multiple-Choice Score/Total Possible Score _____ /34		
Reading – Part 4: Grammar, Usage, Mechanics		
35.	Adjectives	0 1
36.	Adjectives	0 1
37.	Adjectives	0 1
38.	Adverbs	0 1
39.	Adjectives	0 1
40.	Adverbs	0 1
Student's Reading Total Score/Total Possible Score _____ /44		

*L = literal   I = inferential   C = critical analysis

Regrouping (Reading – Parts 1–3) percentage: _____ ÷ 34 = _____ × 100 = _____%
　　　　　　　　　　　　　　　　　　　(student's score)　　　　　　　　　　(percentage score)

Reading – Parts 1–4 percentage score: _____ ÷ 44 = _____ × 100 = _____%
　　　　　　　　　　　　　　　　　(student's total score)　　　　　　　　(percentage score)

Writing – Part 5

Writing Score (Complete one.) _____ /6　　_____ /5　　_____ /4　　_____ /3

Notes/Observations:

Evaluation Chart: Grade 2 – Unit 5 Benchmark Test

Student Name _____ **Date** _____

Reading – Parts 1–4			
Item	**Tested Skill**	**Item Type***	**Score** (circle one)
Reading – Part 1: Comprehension			
1.	Literary Elements: Plot	L	0 1
2.	Literary Elements: Plot	I	0 1
3.	Main Idea	I	0 1
4.	Author's Purpose	C	0 1
5.	Literary Elements: Character	I	0 1
6.	Literary Elements: Theme	C	0 1
7.	Author's Purpose	I	0 1
8.	Genre (Realistic Fiction)	C	0 1
A.	Constructed-Response Text-to-Self Connection		0 1 2
9.	Sequence	L	0 1
10.	Draw Conclusions	I	0 1
11.	Draw Conclusions	I	0 1
12.	Literary Elements: Plot	L	0 1
13.	Literary Elements: Plot	I	0 1
14.	Main Idea	I	0 1
15.	Literary Elements: Theme	C	0 1
16.	Author's Purpose	C	0 1
B.	Constructed-Response Text-to-Text Connection		0 1 2
Reading – Part 2: Vocabulary			
17.	Word Structure: Compound Words		0 1
18.	Word Structure: Suffix -est		0 1
19.	Word Structure: Compound Words		0 1
20.	Word Structure: Endings		0 1
21.	Word Structure: Compound Words		0 1
22.	Word Structure: Endings		0 1
Reading – Part 3: Phonics			
23.	Silent Consonant *kn*		0 1
24.	Silent Consonant *wr*		0 1
25.	Vowel *al*		0 1
26.	Suffix -*ly*		0 1
27.	Prefix *un-*		0 1

	Reading – Part 3: Phonics (continued)		
28.	Silent Consonant *gn*	0	1
29.	Suffix *-ful*	0	1
30.	Consonant Pattern *ph* /f/	0	1
31.	Suffix *-er* (agent)	0	1
32.	Vowel *aw*	0	1
33.	Prefix *re-*	0	1
34.	Consonant Pattern *gh* /f/	0	1
	Student's Regrouping Multiple-Choice Score/Total Possible Score _____ /34		
	Reading – Part 4: Grammar, Usage, Mechanics		
35.	Pronouns	0	1
36.	Pronouns	0	1
37.	Pronouns	0	1
38.	Pronouns	0	1
39.	Pronouns	0	1
40.	Pronouns	0	1
	Student's Reading Total Score/Total Possible Score _____ /44		

*L = literal   I = inferential   C = critical analysis

Regrouping (Reading – Parts 1–3) percentage: _____ ÷ 34 = _____ × 100 = _____%
                                        (student's score)   (percentage score)

Reading – Parts 1–4 percentage score: _____ ÷ 44 = _____ × 100 = _____%
                                     (student's total score)   (percentage score)

Writing – Part 5

Writing Score (Complete one.) _____ /6   _____ /5   _____ /4   _____ /3

Notes/Observations:

Evaluation Chart: Grade 2 – Unit 6 Benchmark Test

Student Name _____ **Date** _____

	Reading – Parts 1–4		
Item	**Tested Skill**	**Item Type***	**Score** (circle one)
Reading – Part 1: Comprehension			
1.	Compare and Contrast	I	0　　1
2.	Main Idea	I	0　　1
3.	Cause and Effect	I	0　　1
4.	Fact and Opinion	I	0　　1
5.	Draw Conclusions	I	0　　1
6.	Cause and Effect	I	0　　1
7.	Fact and Opinion	I	0　　1
8.	Genre (Nonfiction)	C	0　　1
A.	Constructed-Response Text-to-Self Connection		0　　1　　2
9.	Cause and Effect	L	0　　1
10.	Fact and Opinion	I	0　　1
11.	Draw Conclusions	I	0　　1
12.	Main Idea	I	0　　1
13.	Fact and Opinion	I	0　　1
14.	Cause and Effect	I	0　　1
15.	Compare and Contrast	I	0　　1
16.	Author's Purpose	I	0　　1
B.	Constructed-Response Text-to-Text Connection		0　　1　　2
Reading – Part 2: Vocabulary			
17.	Context Clues: Multiple-Meaning Words		0　　1
18.	Context Clues: Multiple-Meaning Words		0　　1
19.	Context Clues: Multiple-Meaning Words		0　　1
20.	Context Clues: Unfamiliar Words		0　　1
21.	Context Clues: Unfamiliar Words		0　　1
22.	Context Clues: Unfamiliar Words		0　　1
Reading – Part 3: Phonics			
23.	Base Words and Ending -est		0　　1
24.	Base Words and Ending -ed		0　　1
25.	Prefix mid-		0　　1
26.	Common Syllable -tion		0　　1
27.	Base Words and Ending -ed		0　　1
28.	Suffix -ness		0　　1

Reading – Part 3: Phonics (continued)			
29.	Common Syllable -tion	0	1
30.	Suffix -less	0	1
31.	Contraction 'd	0	1
32.	Base Words and Ending -er	0	1
33.	Base Words and Ending -ing	0	1
34.	Contraction 're	0	1
Student's Regrouping Multiple-Choice Score/Total Possible Score _____ /34			
Reading – Part 4: Grammar, Usage, Mechanics			
35.	Capitalization	0	1
36.	Punctuation	0	1
37.	Punctuation	0	1
38.	Punctuation	0	1
39.	Capitalization	0	1
40.	Punctuation	0	1
Student's Reading Total Score/Total Possible Score _____ /44			

*L = literal   I = inferential   C = critical analysis

Regrouping (Reading – Parts 1–3) percentage: _____ ÷ 34 = _____ × 100 = _____ %

(student's score)   (percentage score)

Reading – Parts 1–4 percentage score: _____ ÷ 44 = _____ × 100 = _____ %

(student's total score)   (percentage score)

Writing – Part 5

Writing Score (Complete one.) _____ /6 _____ /5 _____ /4 _____ /3

Notes/Observations:

Evaluation Chart: End-of-Year Benchmark Test

Student Name _____ **Date** _____

Reading – Parts 1–4

Item	Tested Skill	Item Type*	Score (Circle one.)	Item	Tested Skill	Score (Circle one.)
Reading – Part 1: Comprehension				28.	Context Clues: Multiple-Meaning Words	0 1
1.	Literary Elements: Character	I	0 1	29.	Context Clues: Unfamiliar Words	0 1
2.	Main Idea	I	0 1	30.	Word Structure: Suffix -ly	0 1
3.	Compare and Contrast	I	0 1	31.	Context Clues: Multiple-Meaning Words	0 1
4.	Sequence	L	0 1	32.	Context Clues: Unfamiliar Words	0 1
5.	Literary Elements: Setting	I	0 1	33.	Context Clues: Antonyms	0 1
6.	Genre (Fantasy)	C	0 1	**Reading – Part 3: Phonics**		
7.	Literary Elements: Plot	I	0 1	34.	Long *i: igh*	0 1
8.	Literary Elements: Theme	C	0 1	35.	Vowel Diphthong *ou, ow* /ou/	0 1
9.	Main Idea and Details	I	0 1	36.	Vowel Patterns: *ew* /oo/ *(moon)*	0 1
10.	Fact and Opinion	C	0 1	37.	Prefix *-un*	0 1
11.	Main Idea and Details	I	0 1	38.	Consonant Sound *ph* /f/	0 1
12.	Draw Conclusions	I	0 1	39.	Long *e: ee, ea*	0 1
13.	Compare and Contrast	L	0 1	40.	Vowel Diphthong *oi, oy* /oi/	0 1
14.	Author's Purpose	C	0 1	41.	Long *o*: CVCe, *oa*	0 1
15.	Draw Conclusions	I	0 1	42.	Base Words and Ending *-ing*	0 1
16.	Fact and Opinion	C	0 1	43.	Syllables: Multisyllabic Words, VCCV + Suffix	0 1
A.	Constructed-Response Item		0 1 2	44.	Comparative Ending *-er*	0 1
17.	Author's Purpose	C	0 1	45.	Ending *-ed*	0 1
18.	Literary Elements: Character	I	0 1	46.	Contraction *n't*	0 1
19.	Literary Elements: Setting	L	0 1	47.	Suffix *-ness*	0 1
20.	Realism/Fantasy	C	0 1	48.	Contraction *'ve*	0 1
21.	Cause and Effect	I	0 1	49.	Silent Consonant *kn*	0 1
22.	Compare and Contrast	L	0 1	50.	Prefix *mid-*	0 1
23.	Sequence	I	0 1	51.	Silent Consonant *wr*	0 1
24.	Cause and Effect	I	0 1	**Reading – Part 4: Grammar, Usage, Mechanics**		
B.	Constructed-Response Item		0 1 2	52.	Verbs	0 1
Reading – Part 2: Vocabulary				53.	Pronouns	0 1
25.	Context Clues: Synonyms		0 1	54.	Adjectives	0 1
26.	Word Structure: Compound Words		0 1	55.	Verbs	0 1
27.	Context Clues: Antonyms		0 1	56.	Verbs	0 1

- -
Evaluation Chart: End-of-Year Benchmark Test

Benchmark Test Teacher's Manual **T37**

Reading – Part 4: Grammar, Usage, Mechanics (continued)						
57.	Punctuation	0	1	59.	Punctuation	0 1
58.	Punctuation	0	1	60.	Punctuation	0 1
Student's Reading Total Score/Total Possible Score					_____/64	

*L = literal   I = inferential   C = critical analysis

Reading – Parts 1–4 percentage score: _____ ÷ 64 = _____ × 100 = _____%
                          (student's total score)   (percentage score)

Writing – Part 5

Writing Score (Complete one.)   _____/6   _____/5   _____/4   _____/3

Notes/Observations:

CLASS RECORD CHART
Unit Benchmark Tests

Teacher Name _____ Class _____

Student Name	Unit 1		Unit 2		Unit 3		Unit 4		Unit 5		Unit 6	
	Pt 1–4	Pt 5	Pt 1–4	Pt 5	Pt 1–4	Pt 5	Pt 1–4	Pt 5	Pt 1–4	Pt 5	Pt 1–4	Pt 5
1.												
2.												
3.												
4.												
5.												
6.												
7.												
8.												
9.												
10.												
11.												
12.												
13.												
14.												
15.												
16.												
17.												
18.												
19.												
20.												
21.												
22.												
23.												
24.												
25.												
26.												
27.												
28.												
29.												
30.												

ANSWER KEYS
Unit 1 Benchmark Test

Reading – Part 1: Comprehension

Passage 1: "A Very Special Lunch"

1. third choice (on the ground in a forest)
2. second choice (Roy the raccoon)
3. second choice (things that could not really happen.)
4. first choice (under)
5. third choice (teaching friends about picnics)
6. second choice (eating your food outside)
7. first choice (friendly)
8. third choice ("A New Kind of Meal")

A. Use the Constructed-Response Scoring Rubric on page T13 to help you assess children's responses. Assign each response a score from 0 to 2.

Possible top response: I would like to go on a picnic at the park with my friend Sam. We would eat lunch and play ball.

Passage 2: "A Letter to a Friend"

9. second choice (They went to the beach.)
10. third choice (They flew on an airplane and drove in a car.)
11. first choice (friends)
12. second choice (The airplane flew very high.)
13. first choice (a large forest)
14. third choice (to tell Travis about his trip)
15. third choice (play in the sand)
16. second choice (tell Travis about the trip)

B. Use the Constructed-Response Scoring Rubric on page T13 to help you assess children's responses. Assign each response a score from 0 to 2.

Possible top response: Roy and Mike both like to have fun outside. The animals are in the forest. Mike is at the ocean.

Reading – Part 2: High-Frequency Words

17. second choice (though)
18. third choice (mother)
19. first choice (very)
20. second choice (friend)
21. first choice (together)
22. third choice (everywhere)

Reading – Part 3: Phonics

23. third choice (black)
24. first choice (spring)
25. second choice (wink)
26. first choice (path)
27. third choice (fed)
28. third choice (coming)
29. second choice (chose)
30. third choice (ride)
31. first choice (string)
32. third choice (when)
33. second choice (getting)
34. first choice (shell)

Reading – Part 4: Grammar, Usage, Mechanics

35. second choice (Bob went to Lea's house.)

36. third choice (Look out!)

37. first choice (Come with me.)

38. second choice (Did you remember your book?)

39. first choice (Dad)

40. third choice (played with a toy duck)

Writing – Part 5

Prompt: Children are asked to write a story about a time they had fun outside. Details of where they were, who was with them, and what they did are to be included.

Scoring: Use one of the Narrative Writing Scoring Rubrics on pages T14–T15 to help you assess children's compositions. Choose one of the four rubrics, and assign each composition a score based on the 6-point, 5-point, 4-point, or 3-point scale.

Unit 2 Benchmark Test

Reading – Part 1: Comprehension

Passage 1: "An Afternoon with Lin"

1. first choice (at her own home)

2. second choice (Lin asked Susan to come to her house for tea.)

3. third choice (Lin and Susan are friends.)

4. first choice (Susan and Lin drank some tea.)

5. third choice (a realistic story that could actually happen.)

6. third choice (polite and nice)

7. second choice (showing that you like them.)

8. first choice (so that we could learn about something new)

A. Use the Constructed-Response Scoring Rubric on page T13 to help you assess children's responses. Assign each response a score from 0 to 2.

Possible top response: I would ask my friend to come to my house. We would eat a snack. We would play in my room.

Passage 2: "Ari Gets Help"

9. second choice (Ari lost his blanket.)

10. third choice (Ari asked his friends for help.)

11. first choice (Someone has a magic blanket that hums.)

12. second choice (She was glad that they helped Ari.)

13. third choice (Ari and his friends had a snack in the cave.)

14. second choice (Someone could lose a favorite blanket.)

15. first choice (so we would know the blanket was happy)

16. second choice (It is a make-believe story about dragons.)

B. Use the Constructed-Response Scoring Rubric on page T13 to help you assess children's responses. Assign each response a score from 0 to 2.

Possible top response: In both stories they have friends, and they eat and drink in the afternoon. One story is about real kids and the other is about dragons.

Reading – Part 2: High-Frequency Words

17. third choice (brought)

18. first choice (either)

19. second choice (Once)

20. second choice (probably)

21. first choice (people)

22. third choice (You're)

Reading – Part 3: Phonics

23. third choice (ate)
24. first choice (families)
25. second choice (third)
26. third choice (I will)
27. first choice (forest)
28. second choice (glasses)
29. first choice (I'm glad)
30. third choice (plain)
31. second choice (couldn't find)
32. second choice (more)
33. third choice (garden)
34. first choice (It is)

Reading – Part 4: Grammar, Usage, Mechanics

35. first choice (Monday)
36. third choice (cakes)
37. second choice (women)
38. second choice (babies)
39. first choice (The teachers' cars are at school.)
40. third choice (He took the girl's toys.)

Writing – Part 5

Prompt: Children are asked to write about teaching their friends how to clean their bedrooms. They are to include at least four things that should be done to clean the bedroom.

Scoring: Use one of the Expository Writing Scoring Rubrics on pages T18–T19 to help you assess children's compositions. Choose one of the four rubrics, and assign each composition a score based on the 6-point, 5-point, 4-point, or 3-point scale.

Unit 3 Benchmark Test

Reading – Part 1: Comprehension

Passage 1: "Maya Makes a Book"

1. third choice (Ana played with them outside.)
2. first choice (Ana ripped them.)
3. second choice (a story about things that could really happen.)
4. second choice (Ana hid them.)
5. first choice (Ana would not damage Maya's books anymore.)
6. second choice (Maya solved her problem with Ana.)
7. first choice (Ana now had her own book to play with.)
8. third choice (Maya, because she made a book for Ana)

A. Use the Constructed-Response Scoring Rubric on page T13 to help you assess children's responses. Assign each response a score from 0 to 2.

Possible top response: My problem was that I couldn't find my homework in the mornings. I made one special place where I always put it when I was done. Then I could find it before school.

Passage 2: "Telling Your Story"

9. second choice (People made up a good way to tell stories to others.)
10. third choice (They wanted a better way to share their stories.)
11. first choice (People cannot be sure just what the pictures mean.)
12. second choice (The other person changes the story a little.)
13. third choice (People told stories out loud to each other.)

14. first choice (after they used pictures)

15. second choice (easy)

16. third choice (to tell us why letters were invented)

B. Use the Constructed Response Scoring Rubric on page T13 to help you assess children's responses. Assign each response a score from 0 to 2.

Possible top response: They both were inventors. Maya and the people who invented letters and words both made stories and books for others to enjoy.

Reading – Part 2: High-Frequency Words

17. second choice (guess)

18. first choice (hours)

19. third choice (picture)

20. second choice (answer)

21. first choice (faraway)

22. third choice (their)

Reading – Part 3: Phonics

23. second choice (replies)

24. first choice (happier)

25. third choice (outside)

26. first choice (hurry)

27. third choice (nicest)

28. second choice (these)

29. third choice (mind)

30. first choice (robot)

31. second choice (street)

32. first choice (know)

33. third choice (sometimes)

34. second choice (cry)

Reading – Part 4: Grammar, Usage, Mechanics

35. second choice (are playing)

36. first choice (rang)

37. third choice (will see)

38. second choice (wash)

39. first choice (We are good friends.)

40. third choice (The policeman is here today.)

Writing – Part 5

Prompt: Children are asked to write about how their actions would be similar to and different from Maya's if their books or toys were being hurt.

Scoring: Use one of the Expository Writing Scoring Rubrics on pages T18–T19 to help you assess children's compositions. Choose one of the four rubrics, and assign each composition a score based on the 6-point, 5-point, 4-point, or 3-point scale.

Unit 4 Benchmark Test

Reading – Part 1: Comprehension

Passage 1: "All About Seeds"

1. third choice (Both start from seeds.)

2. second choice (Both use animals to help them grow.)

3. first choice (It is best to grow vegetables.)

4. second choice (There are many types of seeds.)

5. first choice (Animals help seeds to grow.)

6. third choice (People should plant flowers.)

7. second choice (It tells important facts about real seeds.)

8. first choice (Animals help to scatter seeds around.)

A. Use the Constructed-Response Scoring Rubric on page T13 to help you assess children's responses. Assign each response a score from 0 to 2.

Possible top response: I would plant flower seeds because I think flowers are pretty.

Passage 2: "Max's New School"

9. third choice (Max didn't want to get up.)

10. first choice (He was unhappy about going to a new school.)

11. second choice (at Max's new school)

12. third choice (Changes in your life can be much better than you expect.)

13. second choice (Max knows many kids on the bus.)

14. first choice (join an after-school club)

15. third choice (His new school has after-school clubs.)

16. first choice (Max thought that his new school was good.)

B. Use the Constructed-Response Scoring Rubric on page T13 to help you assess children's responses. Assign each response a score from 0 to 2.

Possible top response: They both do well in a new place.

Reading – Part 2: Vocabulary

17. third choice (a paper used to pay for something)

18. third choice (being full of power)

19. first choice (not known)

20. second choice (helpful)

21. first choice (groups)

22. second choice (finished)

Reading – Part 3: Phonics

23. third choice (pur ple)

24. first choice (foot)

25. third choice (clown)

26. first choice (noise)

27. second choice (moon)

28. first choice (blue)

29. third choice (pound)

30. second choice (new)

31. third choice (pull)

32. second choice (little)

33. third choice (sprout)

34. first choice (wood)

Reading – Part 4 Grammar, Usage, Mechanics

35. third choice (down)

36. first choice (Four)

37. third choice (tonight)

38. second choice (slowly)

39. third choice (fastest)

40. second choice (taller)

Writing – Part 5

Prompt: Children are asked to write a description of what a garden they plant from seeds would be like.

Scoring: Use one of the Descriptive Writing Scoring Rubrics on pages T16–T17 to help you assess children's compositions. Choose one of the four rubrics, and assign each composition a score based on the 6-point, 5-point, 4-point, or 3-point scale.

Unit 5 Benchmark Test

Reading – Part 1: Comprehension

Passage 1: "Bill's Idea"

1. second choice (say he can't take care of a pet.)

2. first choice (He worked hard taking care of other people's pets.)

3. first choice (A boy shows his parents he could take care of a pet.)

4. second choice (to show that Bill could take care of a pet)

5. first choice (determined.)

6. third choice (Hard work gets rewards.)

7. second choice (to tell a story about how a boy gets a pet)

8. third choice (It tells a story about something that could happen.)

A. Use the Constructed-Response Scoring Rubric on page T13 to help you assess children's responses. Assign each response a score from 0 to 2.

   Possible top response: I make my bed every morning.

Passage 2: "Mrs. Miller's Garden"

9. third choice (Beth told her mother about Mrs. Miller's garden.)

10. first choice (She was too ill to take care of it.)

11. second choice (They wanted people to sign up to help.)

12. third choice (They asked people in the park to help.)

13. second choice (Mrs. Miller enjoyed her garden.)

14. first choice ("Kim and Beth Help Out")

15. second choice (It is good to help your neighbors.)

16. third choice (be happy about what the girls did.)

B. Use the Constructed-Response Scoring Rubric on page T13 to help you assess children's responses. Assign each response a score from 0 to 2.

   Possible top response: Bill, Kim, and Beth are alike because they all want to take care of things. Bill takes care of animals. Kim and Beth take care of a garden. They all do a good job.

Reading – Part 2: Vocabulary

17. third choice (outside)

18. first choice (best)

19. third choice (everyone)

20. second choice (People began calling.)

21. second choice (between 12 noon and dark)

22. third choice (walked)

Reading – Part 3: Phonics

23. first choice (not)

24. third choice (red)

25. second choice (tall)

26. first choice (in a fast way)

27. second choice (not able)

28. first choice (line)

29. third choice (full of beauty)

30. second choice (four)

31. first choice (a tool that clips)

32. second choice (draw)

33. third choice (redo)

34. first choice (off)

Reading – Part 4: Grammar, Usage, Mechanics

35. second choice (He goes to school.)

36. third choice (They take a walk.)

37. first choice (She's going home.)

38. second choice (I will wait for you.)

39. first choice (Tony and I like to go to the park.)

40. third choice (Juan talked with Carl and me.)

Writing – Part 5

Prompt: Children are asked to write a letter to their parents to persuade them to allow child to have a pet. The letter is to contain three things as proof that child could take care of the pet.

Scoring: Use one of the Persuasive Writing Scoring Rubrics on pages T20–T21 to help you assess children's compositions. Choose one of the four rubrics, and assign each composition a score based on the 6-point, 5-point, 4-point, or 3-point scale.

Unit 6 Benchmark Test

Reading – Part 1: Comprehension

Passage 1: "Happy Birthday, United States of America!"

1. second choice (Both had parades.)

2. second choice (how people celebrate Independence Day)

3. third choice (the fireworks going off)

4. second choice (On July 4, 1776, we said that we did not want to be ruled by Great Britain.)

5. first choice (It is a day that marks our country's independence.)

6. third choice (the booms from the fireworks)

7. second choice (The Fourth of July is the best holiday of the whole year.)

8. first choice (It gives information about real people and events.)

A. Use the Constructed-Response Scoring Rubric on page T13 to help you assess children's responses. Assign each response a score from 0 to 2.

Possible top response might be: My family goes to see fireworks every year.

Passage 2: "Family Traditions"

9. third choice (it makes each family different from other families.)

10. second choice (The best memories are family vacations.)

11. first choice (Families make their own special traditions.)

12. third choice (Traditions give family members a good feeling.)

13. second choice (Some families explore the outdoors together.)

14. first choice (Their homes are kept clean and nice.)

15. second choice (Both help families feel connected.)

16. third choice (to tell about things that families can do together)

B. Use the Constructed-Response Scoring Rubric on page T13 to help you assess children's responses. Assign each response a score from 0 to 2.

Possible top response: Families can always go to see the parade together.

Reading – Part 2: Vocabulary

17. first choice (not easy)
18. first choice (count)
19. second choice (again)
20. third choice (free)
21. third choice (people)
22. second choice (told what to do)

Reading – Part 3: Phonics

23. third choice (most loud)
24. second choice (did fire)
25. second choice (midday)
26. first choice (lotion)
27. third choice (connected)
28. first choice (togetherness)
29. second choice (celebrate)
30. first choice (without hope)
31. third choice (we would)
32. second choice (more close)
33. third choice (riding)
34. second choice (you are)

Reading – Part 4: Grammar, Usage, Mechanics

35. second choice (On Monday it will snow.)
36. third choice (Marla said, "We are going away.")
37. first choice (There were lions, tigers, bears, and monkeys at the zoo.)
38. second choice (It rained all day, but it did not thunder.)
39. first choice (We always visit Mrs. Miller on Memorial Day.)
40. third choice (February 28, 2006)

Writing – Part 5

Prompt: Children are asked to write a story about how they and their family celebrated July Fourth last year. The story can be real or made up.

Scoring: Use one of the Narrative Writing Scoring Rubrics on pages T14–T15 to help you assess children's compositions. Choose one of the four rubrics, and assign each composition a score based on the 6-point, 5-point, 4-point, or 3-point scale.

End-of-Year Benchmark Test

Reading – Part 1: Comprehension

Passage 1: "Oscar's Problem"

1. third choice (caring.)
2. third choice ("A Party for Oscar")
3. second choice (He slept all night.)
4. third choice (Oscar's friends talked to Olivia.)
5. first choice (morning)
6. second choice (a fantasy.)
7. third choice (slept like other owls.)
8. second choice (With help, we can change.)

Passage 2: "Whoooo Has Big Feathers?"

9. second choice (what owls' feathers are like.)
10. second choice (Owl feathers bring good luck.)
11. third choice (a white owl in a snowy place)
12. second choice (need their feathers.)
13. third choice (a warm blanket.)
14. third choice (teach you facts about owls.)
15. second choice (Other animals cannot see them very easily.)
16. first choice (Owls stay the same color.)

A. Use the Constructed-Response Scoring Rubric on page T13 to help you assess children's responses. Assign each response a score from 0 to 2.

A possible top response might be:

"Oscar's Problem" has make-believe owls that talk, eat stew, and wear shirts. "Whoooo Has Big Feathers?" has real owls that live in the real world.

Passage 3: "A Letter to Kathy"

17. third choice (hear the sound of an owl flying.)

18. second choice (likes to send and get letters.)

19. first choice (in her bedroom)

20. second choice (Sophie flies away with the owl.)

21. second choice (The owl was blinking its eyes.)

22. third choice (a basketball.)

23. first choice (She saw lights in the tree.)

24. third choice (Kathy to see how the owl looked.)

B. Use the Constructed-Response Scoring Rubric on page T13 to help you assess children's responses. Assign each response a score from 0 to 2.

A possible top response might be:

Both the snowy owl and the great gray owl are covered in feathers and lose their feathers every year. They are different colors and live in different habitats.

Reading – Part 2: Vocabulary

25. second choice (looking hard)

26. first choice (basketball)

27. third choice (quiet)

28. first choice (part of a tree.)

29. second choice (tell each other.)

30. third choice (how he danced.)

31. third choice (without moving)

32. second choice (where the owl lives.)

33. third choice (cool)

Reading – Part 3: Phonics

34. second choice (mice)

35. first choice (sound)

36. third choice (hoot)

37. third choice (unhappy)

38. second choice (funny)

39. second choice (sneak)

40. first choice (joy)

41. first choice (coat)

42. second choice (tap)

43. first choice (sud / den / ly)

44. second choice (bigger)

45. second choice (did peek)

46. third choice (cannot)

47. first choice (dark)

48. second choice (you have)

49. first choice (name)

50. third choice (the middle of the night)

51. third choice (really)

Reading – Part 4: Grammar, Usage, Mechanics

52. third choice (eat)

53. first choice (I)

54. second choice (bigger)

55. third choice (are)

56. second choice (was)

57. third choice (Some owls have white feathers, and others have brown feathers.)

58. first choice (When Sophie saw the owl, she said, "Wow!")

59. third choice (We saw owls, robins, crows, and hawks.)

60. second choice (The owl's feathers are gray.)

Writing – Part 5

Prompt: Children are asked to describe something they looked at for a long time. The description is to include where they were and what they saw.

Scoring: Use one of the Narrative Writing Scoring Rubrics on pages T14–T15 to help you assess children's compositions. Choose one of the four rubrics, and assign each composition a score based on the 6-point, 5-point, 4-point, or 3-point scale.

OPTIONAL — FLUENCY CHECKS OR RUNNING RECORDS

How to Administer and Score a Fluency Test

A fluency test measures a child's reading rate, or the number of correctly read words per minute (wcpm), on grade-level text the child has not seen before. Give the child a copy of the Student Copy of the passage for the test and make a copy of the Teacher Copy for yourself, noting the formula for calculation at the bottom of the page. The Teacher Copy has a scale of running numbers to make it easier for you to know how many words the child read during the fluency check, while the passages in the student edition do not have the numbers. Make sure you have put the child's name and the test date at the top of your copy of the passage. Have a watch or clock available for timing the reading.

Have the child read the text aloud. Do not have the child read the title as part of the fluency reading; it is not included in the running word count. (You may want to tape-record the child's reading for later evaluation.) Stop the child at exactly one minute and note precisely where the child stopped.

As the child reads orally, on your copy of the text, mark any miscues or errors the child makes during the reading (see the chart on page T51). Count the total number of words the child read in a minute. Subtract any words the child read incorrectly. Record the words correct per minute score on the test.

The formula is: Total # of words read – # of errors = words correct per minute (wcpm).

How to Identify Reading Miscues/Errors

Using the passage on page T52, the chart below shows the kinds of miscues and errors to look for as a child reads aloud and the notations to use to mark them.

Reading Miscue	Notations
Omission The child omits words or word parts.	He likes to put his feet in ⊙the⊙ sand.
Substitution The child substitutes words or parts of words for the words in the text.	He likes to hear the ~~waves.~~ *water*
Insertion The child inserts words or parts of words that are not in the text.	He likes to see the birds ^*fly* in the sky.
Mispronunciation/Misreading The child pronounces or reads a word incorrectly.	Zhou saw the face *growing* going up and down in the waves.
Hesitation The child hesitates over a word and the teacher provides the word.	*H* <u>Zhou</u> likes to be near the ocean.
Self-correction The child reads a word incorrectly but then corrects the error.	One day, Zhou saw a (SC) little face in the water.

Notes

- If the child hesitates over a word, wait several seconds before telling the child what the word is.

- If a child makes the same error more than once, count it as only one error.

- Self-correction is not counted as an actual error. However, writing "SC" over the word or words will help you identify words that give the child some difficulty.

Sample Fluency Test

Here is the passage marked as shown on the previous page. As the child reads the passage aloud to you, mark miscues and errors. Have the child read for exactly one minute, and then mark the last word the child reads.

Name *Susan*   *9/4/2009*

What Is It?

H
Zhou likes to be near the ocean. He likes to hear the ~~waves~~ *water*. He likes   15

to put his feet in (the) sand. He likes to see the birds *fly* in the sky.   31

One day, Zhou saw a little face in the water. The face was dark gray. (sc)   46

The face had black eyes and a long nose like a dog. Zhou saw the face   62

growing going up and down in/the waves.   69

"Look! Look!" Zhou said to Mom.   75

Mom stopped reading her book.   80

"What is it?" Zhou asked.   85

"It is a seal," Mom said. "Seals like to swim in the ocean. They look   100

for fish to eat in the water."   107

"I like to swim in the ocean too!" Zhou said.   117

67 - 5 = 62

Interpreting the Results

According to published norms for oral reading fluency, children at the end of Grade 2 should be reading fluently at 90 words correct per minute in text that is on grade level. This chart gives recommended progress toward that goal.

End of Unit/Grade		Reading Rate (wcpm)
Grade 2	Unit 1	50 to 60
Grade 2	Unit 2	58 to 68
Grade 2	Unit 3	66 to 76
Grade 2	Unit 4	74 to 84
Grade 2	Unit 5	82 to 92
Grade 2	Unit 6	90 to 100
End-of-Year Goal		90

If a child's reading rate is lower than the suggested progress toward the standard for his or her grade level, your notes on the child's miscues may help you determine why the rate is low. Does the child make errors that indicate his or her decoding skills are poor? If so, further instruction in phonics may be needed. Do the errors reflect a lack of comprehension or limited vocabulary? In that case, instruction in comprehension strategies and exposure to more vocabulary words may help. A lack of fluency may indicate a lack of exposure to models of fluent oral reading. It may also mean that the child isn't reading enough material at his or her reading level.

How to Take a Running Record

A Running Record is an assessment of oral reading accuracy and oral reading fluency. A child's reading accuracy is based on the number of words read correctly. This measure is determined by an analysis of the errors a child makes—a miscue analysis. Reading fluency is based on reading rate (the number of words read per minute) and the degree to which the child reads with a "natural flow."

A Running Record may be taken using any reading selection at any time. However, the most valid and reliable assessment fulfills these requirements: (1) the text is appropriate to the child's reading level and interest; (2) the text is unfamiliar to the child. The passages in this section are well-suited for use as either a Fluency Test or with a Running Record because they fit these requirements. For additional administrations that involve a Running Record, you may choose other passages from grade-level appropriate texts.

The Running Record may be used to verify instructional decisions suggested by other assessments, such as a Baseline Group or Benchmark Test. It may also be used to identify a child's particular strengths and weaknesses in reading and language development. In addition, the Running Record may be administered periodically throughout the year as a means of monitoring a child's progress.

Measuring oral reading accuracy and oral reading fluency may be accomplished in a single reading, but two different operations are required. The guidelines on pages T54 and T55 explain how to determine each measurement.

How to Measure Oral Reading Accuracy

1. Choose an appropriate grade-level text of about 100 to 200 words, or use those passages that have been provided for use as a Fluency Test.

2. Make copies of the text—one (of the Student Copy) for the child and one (of the Teacher Copy) for you. If the text appears in a book, you may have the child read the text from the book.

3. Give the text to the child and have the child read the text aloud. (You may want to tape-record the child's reading for later evaluation. This approach can be especially helpful if you are timing the child's reading or conducting other assessments at the same time.)

4. Your hand should always be "running" on your copy of the text. Put a checkmark above every word the child reads correctly. Mark any miscues or errors the child makes during the reading (see the explanation of reading miscues/errors listed for Fluency Tests).

5. Count the total number of errors the child makes and find the percentage score for the number of errors. If you are using a passage from this book of Fluency/Running Record Passages, the total word count is indicated for each passage and a formula for determining a percentage score is provided.

6. If you are using a text from a different source, use this formula to get a percentage score:

$$\frac{\text{Total \# of words minus \# of errors}}{\text{Total \# of words}} \times 100 = \text{percentage score}$$

Example: Suppose a child reads a text of 110 words and makes 6 errors.

$$\frac{110 - 6 = 104 \text{ words}}{110} = 0.945 \qquad 0.945 \times 100 = 94.5\% \text{ (round to 95\%)}$$

The percentage score indicates the child's oral reading accuracy (percentage of words in the passage read correctly).

© Pearson Education 2

How to Measure Reading Rate

Reading rate is generally defined as number of words per minute (wpm). To determine the reading rate, follow steps 1–3 as described on page T54. Note the exact time when the child begins reading and the time when he or she finishes.

To calculate the number of words per minute, use the formula below:

$$\frac{\text{Total \# of words read}}{\text{\# of seconds}} \times 60 = \text{words per minute}$$

Example: Suppose a child reads a passage of 120 words in 90 seconds.

$$\frac{120}{90} = 1.33 \text{ (round to the nearest hundredth)}$$

$1.33 \times 60 = 79.8$ words per minute (round to 80 wpm)

Interpreting the Results

For oral reading accuracy, use the following criteria:

- A child who reads 98% – 100% of the words correctly is reading at an independent level and may need more challenging texts.

- A child who reads 91% – 97% of the words correctly is reading at an instructional level and will likely benefit from guided on-level instruction in the regular program.

- A child who reads with an accuracy of 90% or less is reading at a frustration level and may benefit most from targeted instruction with lower-level texts or strategic intervention.

For any child whose Running Record results are not clearly definitive, we recommend administering additional individual assessments, such as classroom observations and anecdotal records. For more information about other assessments, refer to the *Assessment Handbook.*

On the following pages you will find passages that may be used for either Fluency or Running Record Tests, indicated by grade and unit. Both a Teacher Copy and a Student Copy have been provided.

Student Name _____ Date _____

Where Is Ben's Kitten?

Ben's fuzzy new kitten was lost. Ben looked everywhere for her. He looked	13
all over the house. He looked under every bed. He even looked in his toy box. His	30
kitten was nowhere to be found.	36
Ben's mother said, "Don't worry. I'm sure she has found a warm place for	50
a nap."	52
But Ben was worried. It was a cold, snowy day. What if his kitten had gone	68
outside? So Ben went outside. He called for her in the snow. There was no answer.	84
When Ben got home, his feet felt like ice. He went to put on his fuzzy slippers.	101
That's when he saw a fuzzy tail. His kitten had found a warm place for a nap. She	119
was inside his slipper.	123

Fluency Test

☐ – ☐ = ☐ (wcpm)

Running Record

Oral Reading Accuracy:

Reading Rate:

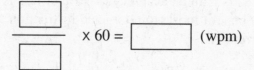

Where Is Ben's Kitten?

Ben's fuzzy new kitten was lost. Ben looked everywhere for her. He looked all over the house. He looked under every bed. He even looked in his toy box. His kitten was nowhere to be found.

Ben's mother said, "Don't worry. I'm sure she has found a warm place for a nap."

But Ben was worried. It was a cold, snowy day. What if his kitten had gone outside? So Ben went outside. He called for her in the snow. There was no answer.

When Ben got home, his feet felt like ice. He went to put on his fuzzy slippers. That's when he saw a fuzzy tail. His kitten had found a warm place for a nap. She was inside his slipper.

Student Name _____ Date _____

The Peanut Plant

Peanuts are not real nuts. They are beans. If they were nuts, they would grow on	16
trees. Instead, they grow in the ground.	23
Peanut farms are found only in warm places where there is no ice or snow. The	39
peanut plants must be started every year from seed. As the plants grow, yellow	53
flowers open. A special part on each flower pushes into the ground. There it grows	68
into a peanut.	71
Peanuts need plenty of sun as they grow. But they need rain as well. If there is	88
not enough rain, farmers have to water the plants.	97
There is only one way for farmers to see how the peanuts are growing. They	112
have to dig up some plants. They keep doing that until the peanuts are ready. Then	128
all the peanuts are dug up at once.	136

Fluency Test

[ ] – [ ] = [ ] (wcpm)

Running Record

Oral Reading Accuracy:

$$\frac{[\quad] - [\quad]}{[\quad]} \times 100 = [\quad]\%$$

Reading Rate:

$$\frac{[\quad]}{[\quad]} \times 60 = [\quad] \text{ (wpm)}$$

The Peanut Plant

Peanuts are not real nuts. They are beans. If they were nuts, they would grow on trees. Instead, they grow in the ground.

Peanut farms are found only in warm places where there is no ice or snow. The peanut plants must be started every year from seed. As the plants grow, yellow flowers open. A special part on each flower pushes into the ground. There it grows into a peanut.

Peanuts need plenty of sun as they grow. But they need rain as well. If there is not enough rain, farmers have to water the plants.

There is only one way for farmers to see how the peanuts are growing. They have to dig up some plants. They keep doing that until the peanuts are ready. Then all the peanuts are dug up at once.

Student Name _____ **Date** _____

The Very Proud King

Long ago, there was a very proud king who went around with his nose in the	16
air. This made it easier to look down on everyone. It also made his crown fall off.	33
And it made him trip over the smallest thing.	42
One day, a brave little boy went right up to him.	53
"Why do you walk around with your nose in the air?" asked the boy.	67
No one had ever asked that before.	74
"Because my father walked around that way, and so did his father before him,"	88
the king answered.	91
"It's a silly thing to do," said the boy.	100
No one had ever said that before.	107
The king stopped in his tracks.	113
Then he said, "Why, you're right. It is silly. Why hasn't anyone ever said that	128
before?"	129
So the king started walking around like everyone else. His crown stayed on his	143
head, and he no longer tripped. That made him prouder than ever.	155

Fluency Test

[ ] – [ ] = [ ] (wcpm)

Running Record

Oral Reading Accuracy: Reading Rate:

$$\frac{[\ ] - [\ ]}{[\ ]} \times 100 = [\quad] \%$$ $$\frac{[\ ]}{[\ ]} \times 60 = [\qquad] \text{(wpm)}$$

The Very Proud King

Long ago, there was a very proud king who went around with his nose in the air. This made it easier to look down on everyone. It also made his crown fall off. And it made him trip over the smallest thing.

One day, a brave little boy went right up to him.

"Why do you walk around with your nose in the air?" asked the boy.

No one had ever asked that before.

"Because my father walked around that way, and so did his father before him," the king answered.

"It's a silly thing to do," said the boy.

No one had ever said that before.

The king stopped in his tracks.

Then he said, "Why, you're right. It is silly. Why hasn't anyone ever said that before?"

So the king started walking around like everyone else. His crown stayed on his head, and he no longer tripped. That made him prouder than ever.

Student Name _____ Date _____

Brave Butterflies

Birds are not the only ones to fly south each winter. Certain butterflies called	14
Monarch butterflies do the same thing. These black-and-orange butterflies live	26
all over the United States, but they head to warm places in winter. Some fly to	42
California, while others fly to Mexico.	48
The butterflies start heading south as soon as the air grows cool. They fly	62
hundreds of miles, but they do not always fly in a straight line. Strong winds can	78
blow butterflies off course. They may also have to fly around mountains. The trip	92
can take months.	95
When the butterflies reach their winter homes, they gather on certain trees. The	108
trees stay covered with butterflies until spring, when the butterflies head north.	120
Each year, people place tags on the wings of some of the butterflies. That way,	135
the butterflies can be tracked. You may even find or see one of them. If you do, get	153
in touch with the group called Monarch Watch. You can help the group learn more	168
about these brave butterflies.	172

Fluency Test

[ ] – [ ] = [ ] (wcpm)

Running Record

Oral Reading Accuracy:

$$\frac{[\quad] - [\quad]}{[\quad]} \times 100 = [\quad\%]$$

Reading Rate:

$$\frac{[\quad]}{[\quad]} \times 60 = [\quad] \text{(wpm)}$$

Brave Butterflies

Birds are not the only ones to fly south each winter. Certain butterflies called Monarch butterflies do the same thing. These black-and-orange butterflies live all over the United States, but they head to warm places in winter. Some fly to California, while others fly to Mexico.

The butterflies start heading south as soon as the air grows cool. They fly hundreds of miles, but they do not always fly in a straight line. Strong winds can blow butterflies off course. They may also have to fly around mountains. The trip can take months.

When the butterflies reach their winter homes, they gather on certain trees. The trees stay covered with butterflies until spring, when the butterflies head north.

Each year, people place tags on the wings of some of the butterflies. That way, the butterflies can be tracked. You may even find or see one of them. If you do, get in touch with the group called Monarch Watch. You can help the group learn more about these brave butterflies.

Student Name _____ Date _____

The Wolf and the Dog

A wolf lived deep in the forest. One winter the wolf was starving, so he	15
wandered away from the woods in his hunt for food. All at once he smelled a	31
delicious smell. He followed the tasty smell to a farmyard. There the wolf found a	46
well-fed dog on the end of a long chain. The dog looked at the starving wolf.	63
"Come," he said, "you can share my dinner. I have plenty of food."	76
The wolf said yes to the dog's kind offer. To tell the truth, he gobbled up far	93
more than his fair share. He was, after all, a wolf.	104
After dinner, the wolf politely asked the dog about his heavy chain.	116
"Oh, I don't mind it," said the dog. "Look at all the food I have to eat. You	134
know, you could probably work here too. You could help me scare away strangers."	148
"Would I have to wear a chain?" asked the wolf.	158
"Yes," answered the dog, "but you'll get used to it."	168
"No, thanks," said the wolf as he started to leave. "I'd rather be hungry than be	184
on the end of a chain."	190

Fluency Test

[   ] – [   ] = [   ] (wcpm)

Running Record

Oral Reading Accuracy: Reading Rate:

$$\frac{[\quad] - [\quad]}{[\quad]} \times 100 = [\quad\%\quad] \qquad \frac{[\quad]}{[\quad]} \times 60 = [\quad] \text{ (wpm)}$$

The Wolf and the Dog

A wolf lived deep in the forest. One winter the wolf was starving, so he wandered away from the woods in his hunt for food. All at once he smelled a delicious smell. He followed the tasty smell to a farmyard. There the wolf found a well-fed dog on the end of a long chain. The dog looked at the starving wolf.

"Come," he said, "you can share my dinner. I have plenty of food."

The wolf said yes to the dog's kind offer. To tell the truth, he gobbled up far more than his fair share. He was, after all, a wolf.

After dinner, the wolf politely asked the dog about his heavy chain.

"Oh, I don't mind it," said the dog. "Look at all the food I have to eat. You know, you could probably work here too. You could help me scare away strangers."

"Would I have to wear a chain?" asked the wolf.

"Yes," answered the dog, "but you'll get used to it."

"No, thanks," said the wolf as he started to leave. "I'd rather be hungry than be on the end of a chain."

Student Name _____ Date _____

Grandma Moses

Grandma Moses was a great artist, but she did not become one until she was	15
very old. She painted when she was a little girl, but she had a hard life. Grandma	32
Moses spent almost fifty years as a farmer. She had to take care of her family and	50
had no time for art.	54
When Grandma Moses was in her 70s, she finally had time to herself. She	68
started painting again. She painted happy pictures of farm life in every season. One	82
day, she put her paintings in a store window. A man who collected art bought them	98
all for just a few dollars each. He showed her paintings to other people, and they	114
wanted to buy some, too.	119
Soon Grandma Moses was famous. Her paintings started to sell for a lot of	133
money. But she continued living a simple life on her farm, and she kept painting.	148
Grandma Moses lived to be 101 years old. By then, she had painted hundreds	162
and hundreds of paintings. You can see them in library books and at museums. The	177
paintings show people working on farms. They show people ice-skating and having	189
picnics. Everyone looks happy. Looking at Grandma Moses's paintings can make	200
you happy, too.	203

Fluency Test

[ ] – [ ] = [ ] (wcpm)

Running Record

Oral Reading Accuracy:

$$\frac{[\ \ ] - [\ \ ]}{[\ \ ]} \times 100 = [\quad] \%$$

Reading Rate:

$$\frac{[\ \ ]}{[\ \ ]} \times 60 = [\quad] \text{ (wpm)}$$

© Pearson Education 2

Grandma Moses

Grandma Moses was a great artist, but she did not become one until she was very old. She painted when she was a little girl, but she had a hard life. Grandma Moses spent almost fifty years as a farmer. She had to take care of her family and had no time for art.

When Grandma Moses was in her 70s, she finally had time to herself. She started painting again. She painted happy pictures of farm life in every season. One day, she put her paintings in a store window. A man who collected art bought them all for just a few dollars each. He showed her paintings to other people, and they wanted to buy some, too.

Soon Grandma Moses was famous. Her paintings started to sell for a lot of money. But she continued living a simple life on her farm, and she kept painting.

Grandma Moses lived to be 101 years old. By then, she had painted hundreds and hundreds of paintings. You can see them in library books and at museums. The paintings show people working on farms. They show people ice-skating and having picnics. Everyone looks happy. Looking at Grandma Moses's paintings can make you happy, too.

NAME _____   DATE _____

Scott Foresman
Benchmark Test

Unit 1
Exploration

Reading STREET Grade 2

PEARSON
Scott Foresman

Editorial Offices: Glenview, Illinois • Parsippany, New Jersey
New York, New York
Sales Offices: Boston, Massachusetts • Duluth, Georgia • Glenview, Illinois
Coppell, Texas • Sacramento, California • Mesa, Arizona

9 10 V031 14 13 12 11 10 09 08

ISBN 0-328-19585-5

90000

9 780328 195855

Directions
In this story, three friends have a picnic. Read the story and answer Numbers 1 through 8.

A Very Special Lunch

It was a fine summer day. Fran the fox was walking in the forest when she saw her friend Roy the raccoon. Roy was carrying a basket and a blanket.

"Hello, Roy," said Fran. "What are you doing?"

"I'm going to a picnic," answered Roy.

"What is a picnic?" asked Fran. "Is it a game?"

"No," Roy laughed. "A picnic is different from a game. It is a special kind of lunch. You get to eat outside! Would you like to come?"

"Oh, yes! I'm hungry," said Fran.

Roy and Fran walked together in the forest. Soon they met Ben the bird.

Ben asked Roy and Fran, "What are you doing today?"

"We're going to a picnic," they said.

"What is a picnic?" asked Ben. "Is it a contest?"

"No," Roy answered. "A picnic isn't a contest. It's a lunch that you eat outside. Come with us! You'll see."

Soon the three friends came to a big tree.

"Here is a perfect place for our picnic," said Roy.

Fran and Ben looked everywhere. They didn't see any table or food.

"Where is the picnic?" they asked.

"We have to make the picnic! We'll make it here!" said Roy.

Roy put the blanket on the ground in the shade beneath the tree. Then he opened the basket. He brought out bread, apples, cookies, and milk to drink. Roy set everything on the blanket.

"This is a picnic. Now it's time to eat lunch!" said Roy. "Thank you for coming!"

© Pearson Education 2

1 **Where did the animals have their picnic?**

○ on the playground at school

○ on a table in the park

○ on the ground in a forest

2 **Who knew what a picnic was at the beginning of the story?**

○ Fran the fox

○ Roy the raccoon

○ Ben the bird

3 **This story tells about**

○ animals that could be real.

○ things that could not really happen.

○ real things that happened a long time ago.

4 **The animals had their picnic beneath the tree.**

What word means the same as beneath?

○ under

○ beside

○ near

5 **What was this story all about?**

○ walking in a big forest

○ making special foods to eat

○ teaching friends about picnics

6 **What makes a picnic different from other lunches?**

    ○   eating as fast as you can

    ○   eating your food outside

    ○   talking with your friends

7 **What word best describes Roy?**

    ○   friendly

    ○   sad

    ○   unkind

8 **Which would be another good name for this story?**

    ○   "The Longest Hike"

    ○   "Games to Play Outside"

    ○   "A New Kind of Meal"

Directions

Write your answer to Question A on the lines below. Base your answer on the story "A Very Special Lunch."

A **If you could go on a picnic, where would you go? Who would go with you? Tell about what you would do there.**

_____

- -

_____

_____

- -

_____

- -

_____

_____

- -

_____

- -

_____

_____

- -

_____

- -

_____

A Letter to a Friend

Dear Travis,

   My family is taking a trip. It is fun to be on a trip with them. I miss you though.

   We started our trip by getting on a big airplane. It was very exciting! The airplane was silver. Many people were getting on. My brother, Jack, and I sat together in one row. Father and Mother sat in the row behind us.

GO ON

I sat next to the window on the airplane. I could look down and see where we were. First the airplane flew over the city where we live. All the houses and streets looked very tiny. The cars looked like toys. I tried to see our school, but the airplane flew too fast!

Before long, we flew over a big forest. It looked like a giant green cloth on the ground. The trees were green bumps. I imagined all the animals in the forest. I wondered what they were doing.

After our airplane ride, we drove to a house by the ocean. It is a small house with many windows. I think we will have fun here.

The ocean is near the house. We'll play in the sand every day. My brother brought his toys to use in the sand. Mother says we can go swimming too.

We will come home in two weeks. I'll tell you all about our trip when I see you.

Your friend,

Mike

9 Where did Mike's family go on their trip?

○ They went to a forest.

○ They went to the beach.

○ They went to the park.

10 What two ways did Mike's family travel on their trip?

○ They drove in a car and then swam.

○ They flew on an airplane and walked.

○ They flew on an airplane and drove in a car.

11 Which word best describes Travis and Mike?

○ friends

○ brothers

○ parents

12 Why did the cars look like toys to Mike?

○ The cars were Jack's toys.

○ The airplane flew very high.

○ The ocean was very big.

13 What looked to Mike like a big cloth on the ground?

○ a large forest

○ a long beach

○ the houses and streets

14 Why did Mike write this letter?

○ to ask Travis to come visit

○ to teach Jack about the ocean

○ to tell Travis about his trip

GO ON

15 **What does Mike want to do?**
- ○ read to his brother
- ○ look at the animals
- ○ play in the sand

16 **What does Mike want to do when he gets home?**
- ○ play and swim in the ocean
- ○ tell Travis about the trip
- ○ go back to his school

Directions

Write your answer to Question B on the lines below. Base your answer on the two selections you have read.

B The stories "A Very Special Lunch" and "A Letter to a Friend" tell about doing things outside. How are Roy and Mike the same? How are the settings of the two stories different?

WRITING ACROSS TEXTS

_____

_____

_____

_____

_____

_____

_____

_____

_____

_____

_____

_____

_____

_____

© Pearson Education 2

PART 2: HIGH-FREQUENCY WORDS

Directions
For Numbers 17 through 22, mark the word that best fits in each sentence.

17 We like to play in the snow. It can be fun even _____ it is cold outside.
- ○ straight
- ○ though
- ○ warm

18 Ted asked his _____ if he could have a snack.
- ○ often
- ○ someone
- ○ mother

19 The chocolate cake was _____ good!
- ○ very
- ○ early
- ○ eyes

20 Susan, Lisa, and Kim are my pals. Susan is my best _____ of all.
- ○ front
- ○ friend
- ○ father

21 Dad said, "Let's read a book _____."
- ○ together
- ○ learn
- ○ work

22 Birds are in the yard, in the park, and at our school. Birds seem to be _____.
- ○ somewhere
- ○ world
- ○ everywhere

STOP

PART 3: PHONICS

Directions

For Numbers 23 through 34, find the answer to each question.

23 Roy was carrying a basket and a <u>blanket</u>.

What word has the same beginning sounds as <u>blanket</u>?

◯ thank   ◯ bread   ◯ black

24 Mike wrote, "Before <u>long</u>, we flew over a big forest."

What word has the same ending sound as <u>long</u>?

◯ spring   ◯ dodge   ◯ change

25 Roy set out milk to <u>drink</u>.

What word has the same ending sounds as <u>drink</u>?

◯ thing   ◯ wink   ◯ lunch

26 Roy put the blanket on the ground in the shade <u>beneath</u> the tree.

What word has the same ending sound as <u>beneath</u>?

◯ path   ◯ watch   ◯ great

27 Roy set out <u>bread</u>, apples, cookies, and milk.

What word rhymes with <u>bread</u>?

◯ beach   ◯ need   ◯ fed

28 Which shows the correct way to add <u>ing</u> to the word come?

◯ comeing   ◯ comming   ◯ coming

GO ON

29 Jack brought his toys to <u>use</u> in the sand.

What word has the same ending sound as <u>use</u>?

  ○ place   ○ chose   ○ house

30 In the story, the cars looked <u>like</u> toys.

What word has the same middle sound as <u>like</u>?

  ○ with   ○ trip   ○ ride

31 Mike wrote, "All the houses and <u>streets</u> looked tiny."

What word has the same beginning sounds as <u>streets</u>?

  ○ string   ○ truck   ○ worst

32 On the airplane Mike sat <u>next</u> to the window.

What word has the same middle sound as <u>next</u>?

  ○ need   ○ her   ○ when

33 Find the correct word to fit in this sentence.

Mike saw many people _____ on the airplane.

  ○ geting   ○ getting   ○ geteing

34 Roy put the blanket on the ground in the <u>shade</u> beneath the tree.

What word has the same beginning sound as <u>shade</u>?

  ○ shell   ○ soon   ○ child

PART 4: GRAMMAR, USAGE, MECHANICS

Directions
For Numbers 35 through 40, mark the answer to each sentence.

35 Which one is a complete sentence?
- ○ Going for a walk.
- ○ Bob went to Lea's house.
- ○ Sue and her friend Pat.

36 Which one is an exclamation?
- ○ The plane is landing.
- ○ Are you ready?
- ○ Look out!

37 Which one is a command?
- ○ Come with me.
- ○ Are you alone?
- ○ Jim likes ice cream.

38 Which one is a question?
- ○ Today will be a beautiful day.
- ○ Did you remember your book?
- ○ The little boy was afraid of bears.

39 Which word is the subject of the sentence?

Dad put a glass on the table.

   ○ Dad   ○ glass   ○ table

40 What is the predicate of the sentence?

In the afternoon, the child and his mother played with a toy duck.

   ○ In the afternoon

   ○ the child and his mother

   ○ played with a toy duck

PART 5: WRITING

PROMPT

The stories told about having fun outside. Think about a time you had fun outside.

Write a story about a time you had fun outside. Tell where you were. Tell who was with you. Tell what you did.

CHECKLIST FOR WRITERS

_____ Did I think about a time I had fun outside before I started writing?

_____ Did I tell where I was, who was with me, and what I did?

_____ Does my story have a beginning, middle, and end?

_____ Did I choose my words carefully?

_____ Do my sentences make sense?

_____ Do my sentences start with capital letters?

_____ Do my sentences end with end marks?

_____ Did I check my spelling?

_____ Did I make sure my paper is the way I want readers to read it?

NAME _____ DATE _____

Scott Foresman

Benchmark Test

Unit 2
Working Together

Editorial Offices: Glenview, Illinois • Parsippany, New Jersey
New York, New York
Sales Offices: Boston, Massachusetts • Duluth, Georgia • Glenview, Illinois
Coppell, Texas • Sacramento, California • Mesa, Arizona

Copyright © Pearson Education, Inc.

ISBN 0-328-19586-3

9 10 V031 14 13 12 11 10 09 08

Directions
Read this story about two friends. Then answer Numbers 1 through 8.

An Afternoon with Lin

Lin and Susan are friends. They go to the same school, and they like to play together.

One day Lin asked Susan, "Would you like to come to my house after school tomorrow? My mother will give us tea."

"I've never had tea," answered Susan. "What is it?"

"Tea is a drink made with hot water and dried leaves," replied Lin.

So Susan asked her mother if she could go to Lin's house after school. Her mother said yes.

© Pearson Education 2

"Lin's mother will give us tea," said Susan.

"That will be fun for you," said Susan's mother. "I'll call Lin's mother and ask about this."

Susan's mother called Lin's mother on the telephone.

Lin's mother told Susan's mother, "In China, the country where we used to live, drinking tea was very important. Now we are making new friends and doing new things, but we still like to drink tea and remember our time in China."

The next day, Susan went to Lin's house. Lin showed Susan the small cups that her family brought from China and used for drinking tea. They were very beautiful.

The two girls drank their tea and ate small, sweet cakes.

"Do you like the tea, Susan?" asked Lin.

"I think it's very good," answered Susan. "Thank you for asking me to drink it with you."

"You are a nice girl," said Lin's mother. "I am glad you're Lin's friend."

"And I am glad Lin is my friend!" said Susan.

1 **Where was Lin's mother during the story?**

○ at her own home

○ in China

○ at Lin's school

2 **What happened first?**

○ Susan's mother called Lin's mother on the telephone.

○ Lin asked Susan to come to her house for tea.

○ Lin's mother asked Susan if she liked tea.

3 **Why did Lin ask Susan to come to her house?**

○ Susan asked for some tea.

○ Susan's mother called Lin's mother.

○ Lin and Susan are friends.

4 **What happened after Lin showed the small cups to Susan?**

○ Susan and Lin drank some tea.

○ Lin and her parents came from China.

○ Susan asked to go to Lin's house.

5 **The story "An Afternoon with Lin" is**

○ a fantasy that could never really happen.

○ a make-believe story that could not happen.

○ a realistic story that could actually happen.

6 **Which words describe Susan?**

   ○ noisy and funny

   ○ afraid and disappointed

   ○ polite and nice

7 **Giving someone tea is a sign of**

   ○ wishing they would go home.

   ○ showing that you like them.

   ○ wondering where they are from.

8 **Why did the author tell us about tea?**

   ○ so that we could learn about something new

   ○ because it was a funny thing to write about

   ○ so that we could see how sad Lin was

GO ON

Directions

Write your answer to Question A on the lines below. Base your answer on the story "An Afternoon with Lin."

A   How would you share an afternoon with a friend? What would you do? Where would you go?

_____

_____

_____

_____

_____

_____

_____

_____

_____

_____

_____

_____

Ari Gets Help

Ari is a little green dragon who lives in a nice cool cave with his family. Every afternoon, Ari and his dragon friends play tag in the park. Before he goes to play, Ari has to clean up his part of the cave.

Once when Ari was cleaning up, he could not find his favorite blanket.

"My magic blanket is gone!" he cried to his mother. "What should I do?"

Ari's mother, a big blue dragon named Momo, looked around the cave. She could not find Ari's blanket either.

"I think your blanket probably wanted to go outside," said Momo. "Let's go to the park and ask your friends to help us look for it."

Ari and Momo flew to the park. Ari called out to his friends, "My favorite blanket is lost. Will you help us look for it?"

The dragons flew all over the neighborhood. They found Ari's blanket in a tall tree! The blanket was humming a happy song.

"I think your blanket wanted to see the sun," said one of Ari's friends.

"Maybe I should take it to the park some days," said Ari. "It can watch us play tag."

"I think the blanket could play tag too!" replied Ari's friend.

Momo said, "Thank you all for helping Ari! Please come to our cave for milk and cake."

All the little dragons went to the cave that afternoon. They put their glasses of milk and plates of cake on the magic blanket, which hummed happily.

9 **What happened first?**

   ○ Ari asked for help.

   ○ Ari lost his blanket.

   ○ Momo helped Ari.

10 **What happened next after Ari and his mother went to the park?**

   ○ Momo asked her friends for help.

   ○ Ari's friends asked him for help.

   ○ Ari asked his friends for help.

11 **Which one is make-believe?**

   ○ Someone has a magic blanket that hums.

   ○ Someone must do chores before going out to play.

   ○ Someone likes to play with friends after school.

12 **How did Momo feel about Ari's friends?**

   ○ She was mad because they ate too much.

   ○ She was glad that they helped Ari.

   ○ She was sad because they played tag.

13 **Which one happened after the blanket was found?**

   ○ Ari and his friends played tag in the park.

   ○ Ari and Momo looked for Ari's blanket.

   ○ Ari and his friends had a snack in the cave.

14 **Which one could really happen?**

   ○ A blanket could play tag.

   ○ Someone could lose a favorite blanket.

   ○ A blanket could hum a song.

GO ON

15 Why did the writer tell us the blanket hummed?

○ so we would know the blanket was happy

○ so we would think blankets can really hum

○ so we would be careful not to use blankets

16 Which one best describes "Ari Gets Help"?

○ It is a realistic story about real animals.

○ It is a make-believe story about dragons.

○ It is a long poem about a make-believe animal.

Directions

Write your answer to Question B on the lines below. Base your answer on the two selections you have read.

B How are the characters in "An Afternoon with Lin" and "Ari Gets Help" the same? What do they do that is the same? How are they different? Use details from both stories to explain your answer.

PART 2: HIGH-FREQUENCY WORDS

Directions

For Numbers 17 through 22, mark the word that best fits in each sentence.

17 Dad said I could bring a friend to the game. I _____ my pal Steve.

○ break   ○ bought   ○ brought

18 "I'm going shopping," said Pat. "You may _____ stay at home or come along."

○ either   ○ enough   ○ everybody

19 Tim liked to look for shells in the sand. _____ he found a sand dollar!

○ Worst   ○ Once   ○ Above

20 What will Mom give us for a snack? She will _____ give us an apple.

○ promise   ○ probably   ○ brought

21 My parents like to work in the yard. Many other _____ on our street do too.

○ people   ○ pleasant   ○ promise

22 "It's very cold out," Dad told us. "_____ going to need to take your coat."

○ Sorry   ○ Worst   ○ You're

PART 3: PHONICS

Directions

For Numbers 23 through 34, mark the answer to each question.

23 The children like to <u>play</u> together.

What word has the same sound as <u>ay</u> in <u>play</u>?

○ plan

○ happy

○ ate

24 Lin and Susan each have a <u>family</u>.

What is the correct way to write more than one family?

○ families   ○ familyes   ○ familes

25 The two <u>girls</u> drank their tea.

What word has the same sound as <u>ir</u> in <u>girls</u>?

○ wire

○ third

○ grill

26 Susan's mother said, "<u>I'll</u> call Lin's mother."

Which means the same as I'll?

○ I would   ○ I am   ○ I will

27 Drinking tea was <u>important</u> to Lin's family.

What word has the same sound as <u>or</u> in <u>important</u>?

○ forest

○ farther

○ front

GO ON

28 Each dragon has a <u>glass</u> of milk.

What is the correct way to write <u>more than one glass</u>?

○ glasss

○ glasses

○ glases

29 Lin's mother said, "I am <u>glad</u> you are Lin's friend."

What is another way to write <u>I am glad</u>?

○ I'm glad   ○ I'll glad   ○ I'd glad

30 Ari lives in a nice cool <u>cave</u>.

What word has the same sound as the <u>a</u> in c<u>a</u>ve?

○ rabbit

○ magic

○ plain

31 Ari <u>could not find</u> his favorite blanket.

What is another way to write <u>could not find</u>?

○ could'nt find   ○ couldn't find   ○ can't not find

32 <u>Be</u>fore he goes to play, Ari has to clean up.

What word has the same sound as <u>ore</u> in bef<u>ore</u>?

○ discover

○ more

○ another

33 Ari and his dragon friends play tag in the <u>park</u>.

What word has the same sound as <u>ar</u> in <u>park</u>?

- ○ care
- ○ early
- ○ garden

34 Susan said, "<u>It's</u> very good."

What is another way to write It's?

- ○ It is
- ○ It will
- ○ It was

PART 4: GRAMMAR, USAGE, MECHANICS

Directions
For Numbers 35 through 40, mark the answer to each question.

35 **What word is a proper noun?**
- ○ Monday
- ○ yesterday
- ○ tomorrow

36 **What word shows more than one?**
- ○ dress
- ○ happiness
- ○ cakes

37 **What word correctly shows more than one woman?**
- ○ woman
- ○ women
- ○ woman's

38 **What is the correct word to use in this sentence? Many _____ like to chew on their fingers.**
- ○ baby's
- ○ babies
- ○ babys

39 **Which one correctly shows that many teachers own cars?**
- ○ The teachers' cars are at school.
- ○ The teacher's cars are at school.
- ○ The teachers cars' are at school.

40 **Which one correctly shows that the girl owns the toys?**
- ○ He took the girl toy's.
- ○ He took the girls toys.
- ○ He took the girl's toys.

PART 5: WRITING

PROMPT

Pretend you are teaching your friends how to clean their bedrooms. Tell them what they need to do to get their rooms cleaned up. Tell them at least four things they should do.

CHECKLIST FOR WRITERS

_____ Did I plan my paper before I started writing?

_____ Did I tell how to clean a bedroom?

_____ Did I write about four things to do?

_____ Did I put the steps in the right order?

_____ Did I use good action words to tell what they should do?

_____ Do my sentences make sense?

_____ Do my sentences start with capital letters?

_____ Do my sentences end with end marks?

_____ Did I check my spelling?

_____ Did I make sure my paper is the way I want readers to read it?

NAME _____ DATE _____

Scott Foresman
Benchmark Test

Unit 3
Creative Ideas

Editorial Offices: Glenview, Illinois • Parsippany, New Jersey
New York, New York
Sales Offices: Boston, Massachusetts • Duluth, Georgia • Glenview, Illinois
Coppell, Texas • Sacramento, California • Mesa, Arizona

ISBN 0-328-19587-1

9 10 V031 14 13 12 11 10 09 08

Directions

Maya makes a book for her sister. Read about how and why. Then answer Numbers 1 through 8.

Maya Makes a Book

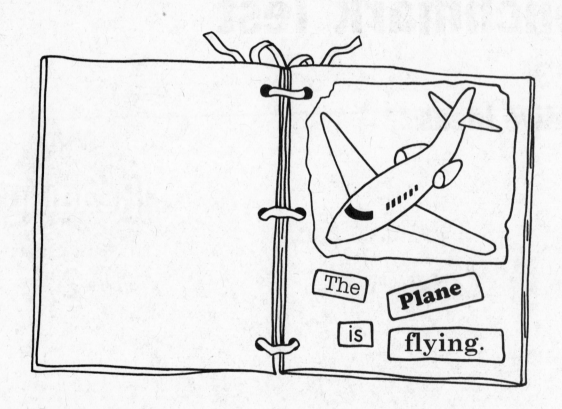

Maya's little sister Ana liked looking at Maya's books. Ana was only three years old, and she didn't know how to take care of books. Ana ripped their pages and took the books outside. The books became torn and dirty. Sometimes Ana even hid Maya's books! Then Maya couldn't find them. Maya didn't like it when her books disappeared or were damaged. She wanted to keep them away from Ana, but she didn't want Ana to be sad.

Maya decided to make a special book for Ana to play with.

"What should I use to make her book?" Maya wondered.

She looked around the house and saw an old telephone book.

"May I have this book?" Maya asked her mother.

"Yes, you may," answered Mother.

Maya cut out pictures for Ana's book. She found a picture of airplanes and pasted it on one page, and then she cut out words and put them under the picture. On another page she put a picture of a girl with a dog. She put words from the telephone book on that page too. She cut out many pictures and made many nice pages.

Mother helped Maya put holes on one edge of each page. Then they tied the pages together with a ribbon.

"What a clever way to make a book!" said Mother. "I am proud of you."

Maya gave Ana the special book, and Ana was very happy. She didn't harm or hide Maya's books anymore. Maya was happy too.

© Pearson Education 2

1 Maya's books became dirty because

○ Maya took them outside and lost them.

○ Mother liked to hide them.

○ Ana played with them outside.

2 How did Maya's books get torn?

○ Ana ripped them.

○ Maya cut out pictures.

○ Maya hid them from Ana.

3 "Maya Makes a Book" is

○ a poem about two girls and their mother.

○ a story about things that could really happen.

○ a fantasy about two children who could not be real.

4 Why did Maya's books disappear?

○ Maya lost them.

○ Ana hid them.

○ Mother put them away.

5 Maya made a special book for Ana so that

○ Ana would not damage Maya's books anymore.

○ Ana would learn how to make a book.

○ Ana would learn how to read some words.

6 **Why was Mother proud of Maya?**

○ Maya was older than Ana.

○ Maya solved her problem with Ana.

○ Maya gave some of her books to Ana.

7 **Why did Ana stop hurting Maya's books?**

○ Ana now had her own book to play with.

○ Maya asked Ana to stop hurting the books.

○ Ana learned she shouldn't hurt Maya's books.

8 **Who solved a problem in "Maya Makes a Book"?**

○ Ana, because she had a new book

○ Mother, because she was proud of Maya

○ Maya, because she made a book for Ana

Directions

Write your answer to Question A on the lines below. Base your answer on the story "Maya Makes a Book."

A Think about a time when you had to solve a problem. What was the problem? What did you do to solve it?

Read about how stories are told. Then answer Numbers 9 through 16.

Telling Your Story

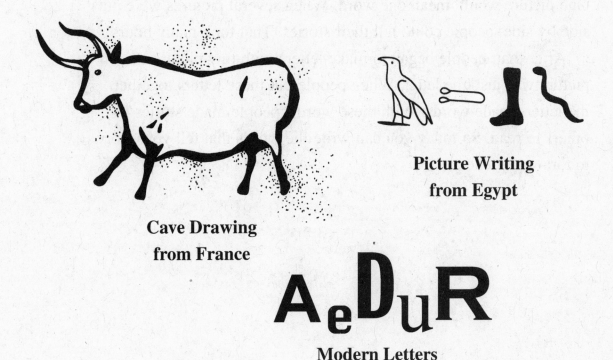

**Cave Drawing
from France**

**Picture Writing
from Egypt**

A_eD_uR

Modern Letters

How would you share a story with friends if they lived far away? Would you call on the telephone? How would you share your story if you lived before people had telephones?

One way to let people know your story is to tell it to one person. The person who hears your story can tell it to others. Then more people can pass it along. One problem is that a story can change a little every time one person tells it to another. Maybe you would be surprised how much your story had changed when it was told back to you!

GO ON

Another way to tell your story is to make pictures showing what happened. A person seeing your pictures may be able to figure out your story. It can be hard to know what pictures mean. People must guess sometimes. It would be better if your story could be shown using words.

Very long ago, people had no way to write any words because they had no letters to use. At first, people started making pictures. One picture would mean one word. When several pictures were put side by side, people could tell their stories. That took many hours!

After that, people began to make letters with tiny pictures. Each picture was just one letter. When people put these letters together, the letters made words. With these words, people made stories for others to read. So today you can write the words that tell your story to faraway friends.

9 **What is "Telling Your Story" all about?**

○ People should listen more carefully to stories.

○ People made up a good way to tell stories to others.

○ Pictures are easier to understand than letters.

10 **Why did people invent written letters and words?**

○ They wanted to tell their stories out loud.

○ They wanted only one person to hear their stories.

○ They wanted a better way to share their stories.

11 **What happens when stories are told in pictures?**

○ People cannot be sure just what the pictures mean.

○ People know that everybody will hear their stories.

○ It is easy for people to tell their stories to others.

12 **What often happens when a person tells a story to someone else?**

○ No one else ever tells the story.

○ The other person changes the story a little.

○ The other person does not hear the story.

13 **Which happened first?**

○ People used pictures to tell stories.

○ People used telephones to tell stories.

○ People told stories out loud to each other.

14 **When did people start to use written letters and words?**

○ after they used pictures

○ after they used telephones

○ before they told any stories

GO ON

15 It can be <u>hard</u> to know what pictures mean.

Which word means the opposite of <u>hard</u> as it is used in this sentence?

- ◯ soft
- ◯ easy
- ◯ different

16 Why did the author write "Telling Your Story"?

- ◯ to teach us how to draw pictures
- ◯ to show us how pictures are made
- ◯ to tell us why letters were invented

Directions

Write your answer to Question B on the lines below. Base your answer on the two selections you have read.

B You read first about the book that Maya made and then about how people invented letters and words for others to read. In what way is Maya the same as the people who invented letters and words long ago?

WRITING ACROSS TEXTS

_____

- -

_____

- -

_____

- -

_____

- -

_____

- -

_____

- -

_____

- -

_____

- -

PART 2: HIGH-FREQUENCY WORDS

Directions
For Numbers 17 through 22, mark the word that best fits in each sentence.

17 "I have a surprise for you," said Dad. "Can you _____ what it is?"
- ○ clothes
- ○ guess
- ○ watch

18 We spent a long time at the park. We played there for _____.
- ○ hours
- ○ only
- ○ half

19 Mother gave me pens in many colors. Then I drew a _____.
- ○ pretty
- ○ believe
- ○ picture

20 The teacher wrote a problem on the board. He asked, "Who has the _____?"
- ○ alone
- ○ answer
- ○ taught

21 We learned about countries across the sea and the people in

_____ lands.

- ○ faraway
- ○ finally
- ○ youngest

22 First the children had naps. Then they all were able to eat

_____ snacks.

- ○ today
- ○ won
- ○ their

PART 3: PHONICS

Directions
For Numbers 23 through 34, mark the answer to each question.

23 Mother and Maya tied the pages together with a ribbon.

What word has the same sound as ie in tied?
- ○ families
- ○ replies
- ○ please

24 Maya was happy too.

What word would mean that Maya was more happy than Ana?
- ○ happier
- ○ happiest
- ○ happily

25 Which one of these words is made up of two smaller words?
- ○ ripped
- ○ pages
- ○ outside

26 The books became torn and dirty.

What word has the same sound as y in dirty?
- ○ hurry
- ○ dry
- ○ joy

27 Maya made many nice pages.

What word would mean that Maya's pages were the most nice of all the pages?
- ○ nicely
- ○ nicer
- ○ nicest

© Pearson Education 2

28 Ana was only <u>three</u> years old.

What word has the same sound as <u>ee</u> in <u>three</u>?

○ bread

○ these

○ fries

29 Maya couldn't <u>find</u> her books.

What word has the same sound as <u>i</u> in <u>find</u>?

○ hint   ○ sing   ○ mind

30 Maya saw an <u>old</u> telephone book.

What word has the same sound as <u>o</u> in <u>old</u>?

○ robot

○ concert

○ doctor

31 People made stories for others to <u>read</u>.

What word has the same sound as <u>ea</u> in <u>read</u>?

○ head   ○ street   ○ heard

32 It would be better if your story could be <u>shown</u> using words.

What word has the same sound as <u>ow</u> in <u>shown</u>?

○ know

○ howl

○ town

33 Which one of these words is made up of two smaller words?

- ○ story
- ○ person
- ○ sometimes

34 Several pictures were put side by side.

What word has the same sound as y in by?

- ○ busy
- ○ cry
- ○ tiny

PART 4: GRAMMAR, USAGE, MECHANICS

Directions
For Numbers 35 through 40, find the answer to each question.

35 Look at this sentence:

Travis and Lee are playing in the house.

Which words tell what is happening now?

- ○ Travis and Lee
- ○ are playing
- ○ in the house

36 Look at this sentence:

The teacher rang the bell for the students.

Which word tells what happened in the past?

- ○ rang
- ○ bell
- ○ students

37 Look at this sentence:

In the park Marie Smith will see her friend.

Which words tell what happens in the future?

- ○ In the park
- ○ Marie Smith
- ○ will see

38 Choose the word that best completes this sentence.

The cat washes its face, and the dogs _____ their paws.

- ○ washes
- ○ wash
- ○ washing

39 Which sentence is written correctly?
- ○ We are good friends.
- ○ We was good friends.
- ○ We am good friends.

40 Which sentence is written correctly?
- ○ The policeman are here today.
- ○ The policeman were here today.
- ○ The policeman is here today.

PART 5: WRITING

PROMPT

What would you do if someone was hurting your books or toys? Tell how that would be different from what Maya did. Tell how your actions would be the same.

CHECKLIST FOR WRITERS

_____ Did I plan my paper before I started writing?

_____ Did I tell what I would do?

_____ Did I tell how that is different from what Maya did?

_____ Did I tell how that is the same as what Maya did?

_____ Did I use good action words to tell what I would do?

_____ Do my sentences make sense?

_____ Do my sentences start with capital letters?

_____ Do my sentences end with end marks?

_____ Did I check my spelling?

_____ Did I make sure my paper is the way I want readers to read it?

NAME _____ DATE _____

Scott Foresman
Benchmark Test
Unit 4
Our Changing World

Editorial Offices: Glenview, Illinois • Parsippany, New Jersey
New York, New York
Sales Offices: Boston, Massachusetts • Duluth, Georgia • Glenview, Illinois
Coppell, Texas • Sacramento, California • Mesa, Arizona

9 10 V031 14 13 12 11 10 09 08

ISBN 0-328-19588-X

90000

9 780328 195886

Directions
Read "All About Seeds" to find out how animals and people can be part of a seed's life. Then answer Numbers 1 through 8.

All About Seeds

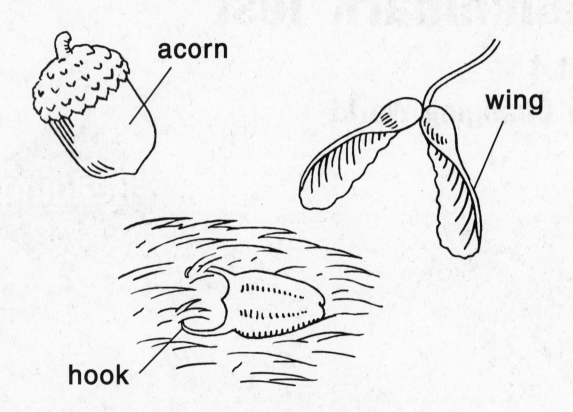

acorn

wing

hook

Seeds come in many different forms and grow into many different kinds of plants. Some seeds become flowers. Other seeds grow into vegetables. Other seeds become bushes or trees. Animals play a big part in helping seeds grow into plants.

Seeds need to be planted far apart from each other. In that way the roots have room to grow stronger, and the plants have more strength and grow larger. Animals help scatter the seeds around.

2

Birds like to eat berries. Sometimes the birds will drop the berry seeds they are eating. When they drop the seeds far away, berry bushes grow in new and different places.

Nuts are seeds too. A chestnut is a seed that comes from a chestnut tree. An acorn is a seed that comes from an oak tree. Animals also help plant these seeds. Squirrels are very busy animals. They hide nuts all over to have food to eat in the winter. Sometimes they do not remember where they have hidden all their nuts. These nuts can grow into trees.

Some seeds have little hooks. The hooks can get caught on an animal's coat. When the seed falls off, it grows where it lands. Some seeds look and move like wings. Maple trees have seeds like this. When wind blows through a maple tree, the seeds fly quickly through the air. They are spread around so that new trees will have lots of room to grow.

Many people like to plant seeds in their gardens. Some people think it is best to grow vegetables such as carrots and peas. Other people have gardens full of beautiful flowers. Whether the plants are flowers, vegetables, or trees, they all started as seeds.

1 **How are flowers and vegetables alike?**
- ○ Both are food.
- ○ Both have hook seeds.
- ○ Both start from seeds.

2 **How are nuts and berry seeds alike?**
- ○ Both have the same shape.
- ○ Both use animals to help them grow.
- ○ Both move in the air.

3 **Which of these is a statement of opinion?**
- ○ It is best to grow vegetables.
- ○ An acorn comes from an oak tree.
- ○ Seeds grow into many kinds of plants.

4 **Which of these is a statement of fact?**
- ○ Oak trees look nicer than maple trees.
- ○ There are many types of seeds.
- ○ Flower gardens are better than vegetable gardens.

5 **What is the main idea of "All About Seeds"?**
- ○ Animals help seeds to grow.
- ○ People like to plant gardens.
- ○ Squirrels bury nuts to plant trees.

6 **Which of these is a statement of opinion?**

- ○ Some seeds have little hooks.
- ○ Squirrels are active animals.
- ○ People should plant flowers.

7 **How can you tell that "All About Seeds" is nonfiction?**

- ○ It tells a funny story about pretend seeds.
- ○ It tells important facts about real seeds.
- ○ It tells a make-believe story about seeds.

8 **Which of these is a statement of fact?**

- ○ Animals help to scatter seeds around.
- ○ Seeds with hooks are better than those with wings.
- ○ Everyone should grow a flower garden.

GO ON

Directions

Write your answer to Question A on the lines below. Base your answer on "All About Seeds."

A   **If you could plant a garden, what kind of seed would you plant? Tell why you would plant this kind of seed.**

_____

_____

_____

_____

_____

_____

_____

_____

_____

_____

_____

_____

Directions

Read about Max's first day at a new school. Then answer Numbers 9 through 16.

Max's New School

Max took his time getting out of bed. He didn't want to go anywhere this morning. The sun was shining, and Max wished he could just spend the whole day playing outside. The summer was over, though. Today was the first day of a new school year.

It was also Max's first day at a new school. During the summer his family had moved to a different part of town. He now lived too far away to go to his old school. Max was sure his new school couldn't be as good as his old one.

© Pearson Education 2

Max got on the school bus and sat down next to a boy named Hal. Max had played baseball with Hal during the summer. Max felt a little better. At least he would know one person at his new school. Then he thought of all his friends at his old school. He missed them.

Max looked around his new classroom. It had computers at the back of the room. His old school didn't have that. Max started to think that maybe this school wouldn't be so bad after all.

The teacher started by playing a game. All the kids had to say something funny about themselves. By the time they finished, everyone in class was laughing. Max thought that his new classmates might become good friends.

At lunch, Hal and some other boys sat with Max. They told him about the after-school clubs. His old school didn't have any clubs. Max thought that maybe things were pretty good at this new school.

When Max got on the bus to go home, he knew many of the kids. As he got off the bus, they all said, "See you tomorrow, Max!" Max was sure he wouldn't have trouble getting out of bed anymore.

9 **How did the story begin?**

○ Max missed his old friends.

○ Max went to his new school.

○ Max didn't want to get up.

10 **How did Max feel at the beginning of the story?**

○ He was unhappy about going to a new school.

○ He was tired from playing baseball.

○ He was ready to make new friends.

11 **Where did the middle part of this story take place?**

○ at Max's old house

○ at Max's new school

○ at Max's baseball field

12 **What is the big idea of this story?**

○ All schools should have computers for the students.

○ Riding on a school bus is the best way to meet new friends.

○ Changes in your life can be much better than you expect.

13 **Which happens last in the story?**

○ Max has lunch with Hal.

○ Max knows many kids on the bus.

○ Max sees computers in his class.

14 **What might Max do next at his new school?**

○ join an after-school club

○ practice baseball with Hal

○ play games with the teacher

GO ON

15 How is Max's new school different from his old school?

○ His new school has a baseball field.

○ His new school does not have computers.

○ His new school has after-school clubs.

16 At the end of the story, how did Max's feelings about school change?

○ Max thought that his new school was good.

○ Max thought his old school was the best.

○ Max thought he would never like his new school.

Directions

Write your answer to Question B on the lines below. Base your answer on the two selections you have read.

B In "All About Seeds" the author tells how seeds grow into plants. In "Max's New School" you see how Max begins to like his new school. Write about how the seeds and Max are the same.

PART 2: VOCABULARY

Directions

For Numbers 17 through 22, mark the answer to each question.

17 Mom gave a **check** to the man at the food store.

What is the meaning of **check** in the sentence above?

- ○ a mark showing that something on a list has been done
- ○ a pattern made of squares
- ○ a paper used to pay for something

18 The **powerful** truck carried rocks to town.

What does **powerful** mean?

- ○ having little power
- ○ being full of rocks
- ○ being full of power

19 Max's new school was **unknown** to him.

What does **unknown** mean?

- ○ not known
- ○ very well known
- ○ soon to be known

20 Other people have gardens full of **beautiful** flowers.

What word has the same suffix as **beautiful**?

- ○ usual
- ○ helpful
- ○ full

21 They told him about the after-school clubs.

What is the meaning of clubs in the sentence above?

○ groups

○ bats

○ hits

22 The summer was over, though.

What does over mean in the sentence above?

○ on top of

○ finished

○ warm

PART 3: PHONICS

Directions

For Numbers 23 through 34, mark the answer to each question.

23 Which of these words is most like the word apple?

- ○ pal
- ○ plate
- ○ purple

24 Some seeds have hooks.

What word has the same middle sound as the oo in hooks?

- ○ foot
- ○ food
- ○ foil

25 Animals move seeds around.

What word has the same sound as the ou in around?

- ○ long
- ○ fond
- ○ clown

26 In "Max's New School," Max has lunch with the boys.

What word rhymes with boys?

- ○ noise
- ○ nose
- ○ noon

27 Max goes to a new school.

What word has the same middle sound as the oo in school?

- ○ house
- ○ moon
- ○ cook

28 Max goes to a <u>new</u> school.

What word rhymes with new?

○ blue

○ blow

○ bled

29 Max sits <u>down</u> next to Hal.

What word has the same sound as the <u>ow</u> in <u>down</u>?

○ grow   ○ pond   ○ pound

30 Nuts are seeds <u>too</u>.

What word rhymes with <u>too</u>?

○ hoe

○ new

○ no

31 Some people have gardens <u>full</u> of beautiful flowers.

What word rhymes with full?

○ doll   Ⓞ ball   ○ pull

32 "All About Seeds" tells about <u>maple</u> trees.

What word has the same number of syllables as <u>maple</u>?

○ mall

○ little

○ unable

33 Max doesn't want to get <u>out</u> of bed.

What word rhymes with <u>out</u>?

○ vote

○ root

○ sprout

34 Max <u>looked</u> around his new class.

What word has the same middle sound as the <u>oo</u> in <u>looked</u>?

○ wood

○ tooth

○ house

PART 4: GRAMMAR, USAGE, MECHANICS

Directions

For Numbers 35 through 40, mark the answer to each question.

35 Which word in this sentence tells <u>where</u>?

He quickly throws the yellow ball down.

- ○ quickly
- ○ yellow
- ○ down

36 Which word in this sentence tells <u>how many</u>?

Four tall trees stand in our front yard.

- ○ Four
- ○ tall
- ○ front

37 Which word in this sentence tells <u>when</u>?

We all are going to a new show tonight.

- ○ all
- ○ new
- ○ tonight

38 Which word in this sentence tells <u>how</u>?

The blue feather floats slowly to the soft ground.

- ○ blue
- ○ slowly
- ○ soft

39 Choose the word that best completes this sentence.

Tom won the school race because he was the
_____ runner.

○ fast
○ faster
○ fastest

40 Choose the word that best completes this sentence.

Jill is _____ than Pam.

○ tall
○ taller
○ tallest

PART 5: WRITING

PROMPT

"All About Seeds" tells about the flowers and vegetables that grow from seeds. Pretend you are going to plant a garden. Think about what your garden would be like. Write a description of your garden.

CHECKLIST FOR WRITERS

_____ Did I plan my paper before I started writing?

_____ Did I tell what my garden would be like?

_____ Did I use words to tell about things I can see, hear, smell, taste, or touch in the garden?

_____ Do my sentences make sense?

_____ Do my sentences start with capital letters?

_____ Do my sentences end with end marks?

_____ Did I check my spelling?

_____ Did I make sure my paper is the way I want readers to read it?

NAME _____ DATE _____

Scott Foresman
Benchmark Test
Unit 5
Responsibilities

PEARSON
Scott
Foresman

Editorial Offices: Glenview, Illinois • Parsippany, New Jersey
New York, New York
Sales Offices: Boston, Massachusetts • Duluth, Georgia • Glenview, Illinois
Coppell, Texas • Sacramento, California • Mesa, Arizona

Copyright © Pearson Education, Inc.

9 10 V031 14 13 12 11 10 09 08

ISBN 0-328-19589-8

90000

9 780328 195893

Directions

Learn how Bill showed that he was ready for a dog. Then answer Numbers 1 through 8.

Bill's Idea

Bill wanted to get a dog. Bill's mother and father didn't think he was old enough. They said, "We just don't think you can take good care of a dog."

Bill decided to show his parents that he could take care of a pet of his own. He thought about the times he had cared for others' pets.

Once when Mrs. Santos went on vacation, he had fed her cat for a week. Another time, when Mr. Jones broke his leg, Bill had walked his dog every afternoon for a month. Bill was sure he knew how to take care of a dog. How could he prove it to his mother and father?

Bill thought and thought. He had an idea! He quickly wrote some signs. He put them up all over the neighborhood.

After a few days the phone started ringing. Mrs. Davis called to ask Bill if he would walk her sheepdog, Bess, before he went to school each morning. Mr. Vega wanted Bill to feed his fish while he was away on a trip. Soon Bill was a very busy boy.

Bill's parents saw that Bill was working very hard taking care of other people's pets. They could see that he was doing a good job. They said, "Bill, now it is time to take care of your own pet."

They all went to the animal shelter to pick out a dog. Bill looked at all the puppies. He picked the one that wagged its tail at him as he walked by the cage. Bill knew that puppy was the one!

It was the greatest day of his life. Bill knew that he could take very good care of his new puppy. He was sure they would have great adventures together.

1 At the beginning of the story, Bill's parents

- ○ say he can have a pet.
- ○ say he can't take care of a pet.
- ○ think he is too old for a pet.

2 What did Bill do to make his parents change their minds?

- ○ He worked hard taking care of other people's pets.
- ○ He walked Mr. Jones's dog every afternoon.
- ○ He went to the animal shelter with his parents.

3 What is the main idea of this story?

- ○ A boy shows his parents he could take care of a pet.
- ○ A boy is sad that his parents won't let him get a dog.
- ○ A boy likes to help other people with their pets.

4 Why did the author tell about the time Bill fed Mrs. Santos's cat?

- ○ to show that a pet is a lot of work
- ○ to show that Bill could take care of a pet
- ○ to show that Bill knew a lot about cats

5 From this story, you can tell that Bill is

- ○ determined.
- ○ unhappy.
- ○ funny.

6 **What did Bill learn in this story?**

○   It is important to help others.

○   When you are busy, you do a good job.

○   Hard work gets rewards.

7 **Why did the author probably write "Bill's Idea"?**

○   to make you want to have a pet

○   to tell a story about how a boy gets a pet

○   to show you how to take care of pets

8 **How can you tell that "Bill's Idea" is realistic fiction?**

○   It tells a true story about what happened to real people.

○   It tells a make-believe story that could not happen.

○   It tells a story about something that could happen.

Directions

Write your answer to Question A on the lines below. Base your answer on "Bill's Idea."

A   **What is one chore you do at home that shows you are growing up?**

© Pearson Education 2

Mrs. Miller's Garden

Kim and Beth lived on the same street, and they did everything together. In the summer they liked to play outdoors and ride their bikes to the park.

One afternoon as they were riding their bikes, they noticed that the house near the park looked run-down. They were surprised. Mrs. Miller, who lived in the house, always had such a nice garden.

When Beth got home, she told her mother about what she had seen. "Mrs. Miller isn't feeling well. She's unable to care for her garden this year," explained Beth's mother.

GO ON

© Pearson Education 2

Beth told Kim, and they decided to help. Kim said, "Let's clean up Mrs. Miller's garden. We can redo it so it is beautiful again."

Kim and Beth rode to Mrs. Miller's house. They started to pick up the dead leaves and branches. It was very hard work. Beth said, "There is too much to clean up here! We can't do it ourselves. We need help."

The girls went to the park and looked at the people there. Kim said, "Let's get everyone in the neighborhood to help. Then we can make Mrs. Miller's garden beautiful."

The next day, Kim and Beth went to the park with a table and a sign. They told everyone who walked by that they needed help. Soon many people had agreed to work in Mrs. Miller's garden.

On Saturday, everyone gathered at Mrs. Miller's house. Some people brought rakes and hoes and clippers. Other people brought new flowers to plant. They worked all day long. By the end of the day, they had given Mrs. Miller her beautiful garden back.

Now when Kim and Beth ride by Mrs. Miller's house, they can see her sitting on her porch. She waves to them and smiles at her wonderful garden.

9 **Which happened first in the story?**

O Kim and Beth cleaned up Mrs. Miller's garden.

O Kim and Beth went to the park with a table.

O Beth told her mother about Mrs. Miller's garden.

10 **Why was Mrs. Miller's garden run-down?**

O She was too ill to take care of it.

O She didn't care about it anymore.

O She was too old to work in it.

11 **Why did Kim and Beth take a table to the park?**

O They wanted to have a picnic.

O They wanted people to sign up to help.

O They wanted to give it to the park.

12 **What did Kim and Beth do after they tried to clean up the garden by themselves?**

O They talked to Beth's mom.

O They played outdoors together.

O They asked people in the park to help.

13 **At the end of the story**

O Kim and Beth cleaned Mrs. Miller's garden.

O Mrs. Miller enjoyed her garden.

O Kim and Beth asked for help.

14 **What would be another good name for this story?**

O "Kim and Beth Help Out"

O "Summertime Fun"

O "How to Plant a Garden"

GO ON

15 What did Kim and Beth learn in this story?

○ It is best to help yourself.

○ It is good to help your neighbors.

○ Children cannot help grown-ups.

16 At the end of this story, the author wanted you to

○ know all about garden work.

○ feel sad for Mrs. Miller.

○ be happy about what the girls did.

Directions

Write your answer to Question B on the lines below. Base your answer on the two selections you have read.

B   In "Bill's Idea" you met Bill. In "Mrs. Miller's Garden" you met Kim and Beth. How are all three children alike?

WRITING ACROSS TEXTS

_____

_____

_____

_____

_____

_____

_____

_____

_____

_____

_____

_____

_____

_____

_____

_____

_____

PART 2: VOCABULARY

Directions
For Numbers 17 through 22, mark the answer to each question.

17 **What is another word for <u>outdoors</u>?**
- ○ outbreak
- ○ outgoing
- ○ outside

18 **What is another word for <u>greatest</u>?**
- ○ best
- ○ better
- ○ good

19 **Which of these is a compound word?**
- ○ beautiful
- ○ clippers
- ○ everyone

20 **What is another way to write this sentence?**

The phone started ringing.
- ○ People will begin to call.
- ○ People began calling.
- ○ People called often.

21 **What is another way to say <u>afternoon</u>?**

    ○ between 8 A.M. and 12 noon

    ○ between 12 noon and dark

    ○ between 12 midnight and 8 A.M.

22 **Which word can be used instead of <u>went</u> in this sentence?**

The girls <u>went</u> to the park.

    ○ walk

    ○ walking

    ○ walked

PART 3: PHONICS

Directions
For Numbers 23 through 34, mark the answer to each question.

23 Bill _knew_ that puppy was the one.

What word has the same beginning sound as _knew_?

○ not   ○ kite   ○ snow

24 Bill _wrote_ some signs.

What word has the same beginning sound as _wrote_?

○ grew   ○ where   ○ red

25 Beth and Kim worked _all_ day long.

What word rhymes with _all_?

○ tail   ○ tall   ○ tale

26 Bill wrote signs _quickly_.

Which of these means the same as _quickly_?

○ in a fast way

○ not in a quick way

○ with care

27 Mrs. Miller is _unable_ to work in her garden.

Which of these means the same as _unable_?

○ just became able

○ not able

○ more able

28 Bill wrote a sign.

What word has the same ending sound as sign?

○ line   ○ wing   ○ change

29 Beth and Kim want to make the garden beautiful.

Which of these means the same as beautiful?

○ without beauty
○ losing beauty
○ full of beauty

30 Bill's phone starts to ring.

What word has the same beginning sound as phone?

○ home   ○ four   ○ post

31 Someone brings clippers for their work in the garden.

Which of these means the same as clippers?

○ a tool that clips
○ a clipping sound
○ to cut something

32 Bill's parents saw that he was doing a good job.

What word rhymes with saw?

○ now   ○ draw   ○ know

33 The girls want to make the garden as nice as it used to be. They want to <u>do it again</u>.

Which of these means the same as the underlined words?

○ overdo

○ undo

○ redo

34 Bill's parents don't think he is old <u>enough</u> to have a pet.

What word has the same ending sound as <u>enough</u>?

○ off

○ thought

○ though

PART 4: GRAMMAR, USAGE, MECHANICS

Directions

For Numbers 35 through 40, mark the answer to each question.

35 Look at this sentence.

Dan goes to school.

Which is another correct way to write this sentence?

○ Him goes to school.

○ He goes to school.

○ They goes to school.

36 Look at this sentence.

Ana and Liz take a walk.

Which is another correct way to write this sentence?

○ She take a walk.

○ Them take a walk.

○ They take a walk.

37 Look at this sentence.

She is going home.

Which is another correct way to write this sentence?

○ She's going home.

○ Shes' going home.

○ Sh'es going home.

38 Look at this sentence.

I'll wait for you.

Which is another correct way to write this sentence?

○ I did wait for you.

○ I will wait for you.

○ I was wait for you.

39 **Which sentence is written correctly?**

○ Tony and I like to go to the park.

○ Tony and me like to go to the park.

○ Me and Tony like to go to the park.

40 **Which sentence is written correctly?**

○ Juan talked with Carl and I.

○ Juan talked with me and Carl.

○ Juan talked with Carl and me.

PART 5: WRITING

PROMPT

In "Bill's Idea," Bill shows his parents that he can take care of a pet. Pretend that you want your parents to let you have a pet of your own. Write a letter to your parents telling three things you would do to prove to them that you could take care of a pet.

CHECKLIST FOR WRITERS

_____ Did I plan my letter before I started writing?

_____ Did I explain that I want a pet?

_____ Did I give three reasons why I could care for it?

_____ Does my letter have an opening and a closing?

_____ Did I sign my letter?

_____ Do my sentences make sense?

_____ Do my sentences start with capital letters?

_____ Do my sentences end with end marks?

_____ Did I check my spelling?

_____ Did I make sure my paper is the way I want readers to read it?

© Pearson Education 2

NAME _____ DATE _____

Scott Foresman
Benchmark Test

Unit 6
Traditions

Editorial Offices: Glenview, Illinois • Parsippany, New Jersey
New York, New York
Sales Offices: Boston, Massachusetts • Duluth, Georgia • Glenview, Illinois
Coppell, Texas • Sacramento, California • Mesa, Arizona

9 10 V031 14 13 12 11 10 09 08

ISBN 0-328-19590-1

90000

Directions

The Fourth of July—Independence Day—is our country's birthday. Read about the holiday. Then answer Numbers 1 through 8.

Happy Birthday, United States of America!

Many people think of the Fourth of July as America's birthday. On that day in 1776, we said that we did not want to be ruled by Great Britain anymore. We would fight to be our own independent country if we had to. So the Fourth of July is called Independence Day.

© Pearson Education 2

Today we celebrate the Fourth of July in many of the same ways that those first citizens did. In 1776, the people of the state of Virginia held parades and fired big guns. In 1777, the people of the city of Philadelphia had a party with fireworks, music, and parades. Before too long, Independence Day was a holiday in every state.

Now, many cities and towns have parades to honor our country's fight for freedom. There are marching bands and people riding in open cars. Everyone waves flags. Many people have a picnic on Independence Day. Other people go to the beach or lake. Often families spend the day together.

After dark comes the most exciting part of the celebration. Cities and towns all over the country set off displays of fireworks. Many times the fireworks are in the colors of our flag—red, white, and blue. People get together under the stars and watch as the beautiful fireworks go off in the air high above. The booms are so loud that some people have to cover their ears. The loudest ones can even make the ground shake.

For some, the Fourth of July is a favorite holiday. It is a day that families get together to celebrate. It is an important holiday too, because it is the day we mark as the beginning of the United States. It is a day that the people of the United States have been celebrating for more than two hundred years!

1 How were the celebrations in 1776 the same as those today?

- ○ Both had people in cars.
- ○ Both had parades.
- ○ Both had fireworks.

2 What is "Happy Birthday, United States of America!" mostly about?

- ○ how the United States got its name
- ○ how people celebrate Independence Day
- ○ how fireworks became a part of the Fourth of July

3 What causes the booms during the Fourth of July celebrations after dark?

- ○ the big guns getting fired
- ○ the many cars in the parades
- ○ the fireworks going off

4 Which of these is a statement of fact?

- ○ The Fourth of July is all Americans' favorite holiday.
- ○ On July 4, 1776, we said that we did not want to be ruled by Great Britain.
- ○ The fireworks are the best part of these holiday celebrations.

5 Why is the Fourth of July such an important holiday for us?

- ○ It is a day that marks our country's independence.
- ○ It is a day families can spend together.
- ○ It is a day for picnics, parades, and fireworks.

6 **What makes the ground shake?**

○ the crowds at the fireworks

○ the noises from the parades

○ the booms from the fireworks

7 **Which of these is a statement of opinion?**

○ The Fourth of July is a day people have celebrated for over 200 years.

○ The Fourth of July is the best holiday of the whole year.

○ Many towns have parades to celebrate the Fourth of July.

8 **How can you tell that "Happy Birthday, United States of America!" is nonfiction?**

○ It gives information about real people and events.

○ It tells a make-believe story that could not happen.

○ It tells a made-up story that could happen.

GO ON

Directions

Write your answer to Question A on the lines below. Base your answer on "Happy Birthday, United States of America!"

A How do you and your family celebrate the Fourth of July? Write a paragraph that tells what you and your family do.

_____

_____

_____

_____

_____

_____

_____

_____

_____

_____

_____

_____

_____

_____

Directions

Read the passage to find out how families all create their own traditions. Then answer Numbers 9 through 16.

Family Traditions

Many families have special things they do together. When families do something special over and over, it becomes part of family life. Having special things to do makes each family different. Family members feel closer to each other too.

Some families have a game night, and everyone gets together to play games. Families can play word or board games, chess or checkers. They may sing or play music together. It doesn't matter exactly what they do. What matters is that they do it together.

Other families have certain times that they all work together. Maybe they work to keep their homes clean and nice. Maybe they help others who need something done. It may not be that the work is fun to do, but at least it is fun doing it together.

There are families that make sure they eat dinner together twice a week. Sometimes this is hard to do because everyone is busy. Children have soccer practice or music lessons, and parents must work late. Still, it is a good idea for families to share a meal together. They can tell each other about their days. It is a good way to keep family members connected.

Still other families like to explore the outdoors together. They go hiking or biking, and they enjoy spending time as a family. Many people say their favorite memories are these family adventures. Maybe it is a trip down to the beach or up to the mountains. Wherever you go, making the trip is even more fun because you are with your family.

Things that families do together all the time are called traditions. They make you feel good about your family. They are the things you will remember all your life.

9 Doing special things together is good for a family because

○ it makes each person in the family work harder.

○ it makes families go out more with each other.

○ it makes each family different from other families.

10 Which of these is a statement of opinion?

○ Traditions are things families do together.

○ The best memories are family vacations.

○ Sometimes parents must work late.

11 What happens when families do the same things together over and over?

○ Families make their own special traditions.

○ Parents always stop working so late.

○ Children do more things after school.

12 What was the main idea of this selection?

○ All families should eat dinner together.

○ Many families remember their adventures.

○ Traditions give family members a good feeling.

13 Which of these is a statement of fact?

○ Working together with your family is a fun thing to do.

○ Some families explore the outdoors together.

○ Families have the most fun eating dinner together.

14 In "Family Traditions," what happens in some families when they all work together?

○ Their homes are kept clean and nice.

○ They become very good at playing soccer.

○ Each person can learn to play music.

15 In "Family Traditions," in what way is a game night the same as a family vacation?

○ Both are done outdoors.

○ Both help families feel connected.

○ Both let children decide what to do.

16 Why did the author probably write this selection?

○ to tell the story of a family's adventure together

○ to show why some families have more fun than others

○ to tell about things that families can do together

Directions

Write your answer to Question B on the lines below. Base your answer on the two selections you have read.

B In "Happy Birthday, United States of America!" you learned about the Fourth of July celebrations. In "Family Traditions" you learned about special things families do together. Write a paragraph that tells one way the Fourth of July can become a family tradition.

WRITING ACROSS TEXTS

_____

_____

_____

_____

_____

_____

_____

_____

_____

_____

_____

_____

_____

_____

PART 2: VOCABULARY

Directions
Find the answer to each question for Numbers 17 through 22.

17 Which meaning of <u>hard</u> is used in this sentence?

Sometimes this is <u>hard</u> to do because everyone is busy.

- ○ not easy
- ○ strong
- ○ bad

18 Which meaning of <u>matter</u> is used in this sentence?

It does <u>matter</u> that they do it together.

- ○ count
- ○ material
- ○ thing

19 Which meaning of <u>over</u> is used in this sentence?

When families do something special <u>over</u> and <u>over</u>, it becomes part of family life.

- ○ above
- ○ again
- ○ higher

20 What does <u>independent</u> mean in this sentence?

We'd fight to be our own <u>independent</u> country if we had to.

- ○ kind of
- ○ island
- ○ free

21 What does <u>citizens</u> mean in this sentence?

We celebrate the Fourth of July in many of the same ways that those first <u>citizens</u> did.

- ○ holidays
- ○ countries
- ○ people

22 What is the meaning of <u>ruled</u> in this sentence?

We did not want to be <u>ruled</u> by Great Britain anymore.

- ○ visited
- ○ told what to do
- ○ measured

PART 3: PHONICS

Directions
For Numbers 23 through 34, find the answer to each question.

23 When you watch fireworks, the <u>loudest</u> booms can make the ground shake.

What of these means the same as <u>loudest</u>?

- ○ least loud
- ○ more loud
- ○ most loud

24 People in 1776 <u>fired</u> big guns.

Which one means the same as <u>fired</u>?

- ○ do fire
- ○ did fire
- ○ will fire

25 On the Fourth of July, people have picnics in the <u>middle of the day</u>.

Which of these means the same as the underlined words?

- ○ misday
- ○ midday
- ○ today

26 "Family Traditions" tells about remembering a <u>vacation</u>.

What word has the same sound as the <u>tion</u> in <u>vacation</u>?

- ○ lotion
- ○ captain
- ○ dandelion

27 The title of the first passage is "Happy Birthday, <u>United</u> States of America!"

Which of these has the same number of syllables as <u>United</u>?

- ○ celebrated
- ○ called
- ○ connected

28 "Family Traditions" tells about a family having a feeling of being together.

Which of these means the same as the underlined words?

○ togetherness

○ togetherless

○ togetherest

29 "Happy Birthday, United States of America!" tells about fireworks celebrations.

What word is the base word of celebrations?

○ ration   ○ celebrate   ○ lebrations

30 Getting everyone in a family together for dinner can seem hopeless.

What words mean the same as hopeless?

○ without hope

○ having hope

○ full of hope

31 In 1776, Americans decided we'd fight to be our own independent country.

Which of these means the same as we'd in this sentence?

○ we did   ○ we had   ○ we would

32 Traditions help family members feel closer to each other.

Which of these means the same as closer?

○ not close

○ more close

○ less close

GO ON

© Pearson Education 2

33 Which word best fits in the sentence?

People were _____ in open cars in the Fourth of July parades.

○ rideing

○ ridding

○ riding

34 Making a trip is more fun when <u>you're</u> with your family.

Which words make up <u>you're</u>?

○ you will

○ you are

○ you would

PART 4: GRAMMAR, USAGE, MECHANICS

Directions
For Numbers 35 through 40, find the answer to each question.

35 Which sentence is written correctly?
- ○ on Monday it will Snow.
- ○ On Monday it will snow.
- ○ On monday it will snow.

36 Which sentence is written correctly?
- ○ "Marla said, We are going away."
- ○ Marla "said We are going away."
- ○ Marla said, "We are going away."

37 Which sentence is written correctly?
- ○ There were lions, tigers, bears, and monkeys at the zoo.
- ○ There were lions, tigers, bears and, monkeys at the zoo.
- ○ There were lions tigers bears and monkeys at the zoo.

38 Which sentence is written correctly?
- ○ It rained all day but it did not thunder.
- ○ It rained all day, but it did not thunder.
- ○ It rained all day but, it did not thunder.

39 **Which sentence is written correctly?**

○ We always visit Mrs. Miller on Memorial Day.

○ We always visit Mrs Miller on Memorial Day.

○ We always visit Mrs. Miller on memorial day.

40 **Which of these is written correctly?**

○ February 28 2006

○ February, 28 2006

○ February 28, 2006

PART 5: WRITING

PROMPT

"Happy Birthday, United States of America!" tells how people celebrate Independence Day. "Family Traditions" tells about things families can do together.

Write a story about how you and your family celebrated the Fourth of July last year. It can be a real story or one you make up.

CHECKLIST FOR WRITERS

_____ Did I plan my story before I started writing?

_____ Does my story tell about my family celebrating July Fourth?

_____ Does my story have a beginning, middle, and end?

_____ Do my sentences make sense?

_____ Do my sentences start with capital letters?

_____ Do my sentences end with end marks?

_____ Did I check my spelling?

_____ Did I make sure my paper is the way I want readers to read it?

NAME _____ DATE _____

Scott Foresman
Benchmark Test
End-of-Year

Editorial Offices: Glenview, Illinois • Parsippany, New Jersey
New York, New York
Sales Offices: Boston, Massachusetts • Duluth, Georgia • Glenview, Illinois
Coppell, Texas • Sacramento, California • Mesa, Arizona

9 10 V031 14 13 12 11 10 09 08

ISBN 0-328-19591-X

90000

9 780328 195916

Directions

Oscar, the owl, had a problem. Read how his friends helped him solve his problem. Then answer Numbers 1 through 8.

Oscar's Problem

Oscar was an owl. Like most owls, he had huge yellow eyes and feathers that stuck up like ears. Oscar was a happy owl, but he had one problem. The other owls in the woods slept all day and hunted at night. Oscar slept all night and stayed awake all day. Because of this, Oscar was often lonely. His friends did not know how to help him change. They took Oscar to see Olivia, a very wise old owl.

Olivia said, "Have a party one night."

"How is a party going to help Oscar sleep all day?" his friends asked.

Olivia laughed. "When the sun begins to set and Oscar starts to fall asleep, start eating, singing, dancing, and laughing," she said. "No one sleeps through a party! Keep him awake all night. He'll be so tired in the morning that he'll fall asleep like the rest of us."

The next night, as the sun set, Oscar yawned. He found a nice spot on an oak branch to sleep. Suddenly, he heard music. Olivia and her husband, Owen, sang a funny song. Owls from all over flew in. Aunt Opal served a mouse stew. Everyone was hooting and talking and having fun. Soon, Oscar saw a big full moon that lit the black night.

At about midnight, Oscar felt sleepy. Suddenly, the band grew louder and everyone began to dance. "Come on, Oscar!" they yelled. "Start tapping those toes!"

Oscar loved to dance. He danced fast, and he danced slowly. He danced with Omar, and he danced with Opal. He danced until the sun peeked over the hills.

"I've never been so tired," Oscar said as he let his yellow eyes close.

The party worked! From that day on, Oscar slept all day and stayed awake all night.

1 **Oscar's friends were**
- ○ angry.
- ○ lazy.
- ○ caring.

2 If this story needed a new name, which name would be best?

○ "Oscar Helps Olivia"

○ "All About Owls"

○ "A Party for Oscar"

3 At the beginning of the story, how was Oscar different from the other owls?

○ He liked to dance.

○ He slept all night.

○ He had yellow eyes.

4 Which happened first in this story?

○ Olivia and Owen sang.

○ Everyone danced.

○ Oscar's friends talked to Olivia.

5 The story ended at what time of day?

○ morning

○ noon

○ evening

6 "Oscar's Problem" is

○ a realistic story.

○ a fantasy.

○ nonfiction.

7 At the end of the story, Oscar
- ○ still slept all night.
- ○ could not fall asleep.
- ○ slept like the other owls.

8 What is the big idea of the story?
- ○ Friends can be mean.
- ○ With help, we can change.
- ○ Sleep is very important.

Whoooo Has Big Feathers?

If you have ever seen an owl, you know that it is a big bird. Owls are covered with feathers from top to bottom. The feathers of an owl are like a big puffy coat. Like coats, feathers keep owls warm. Also like coats, feathers make owls look bigger than they really are.

Every year, owls lose all their feathers and grow new ones. Their feathers don't all fall out at once. Owls lose one feather here and another feather there. Owl feathers are long and strong, and they are brown, gray, and white. There is a legend that says it's good luck to find an owl feather in the woods. Close to their bodies, owls are wrapped in a layer of soft, thick feathers. This layer helps keep owls warm, like a built-in blanket.

Every owl stays the same color through its whole life. The colors of the owl's feathers are the same colors as its habitat. For example, snowy owls have white feathers to help them hide in the snow. Owls in forests have dark feathers that match the dark trees. Owls in open meadows grow tan feathers. Owls' feathers help them blend in, so other animals can't see them. In that way, owls can sneak up on the mice and squirrels they hunt for food. Blending in also keeps owls safe from animals that might harm them.

If you were like an owl and wanted to blend into where you live, what colors would your feathers be?

9 **This selection is mostly about**
- ○ what owls use for food.
- ○ what owls' feathers are like.
- ○ how owls blend in.

10 **Which of the following is a statement of opinion?**
- ○ Owls lose their feathers.
- ○ Owl feathers bring good luck.
- ○ Owls hunt mice for food.

11 **Which of these is an example of blending in?**
- ○ a soft, thick layer of feathers
- ○ finding an owl feather in the woods
- ○ a white owl in a snowy place

GO ON

12 You can tell that owls
- ○ are usually tan.
- ○ need their feathers.
- ○ like to play.

13 The author compared the owl's soft, thick feathers to
- ○ a warm wool hat.
- ○ a brown and white sweater.
- ○ a warm blanket.

14 The author most likely wrote this selection to
- ○ show you how owls hunt.
- ○ tell you why owls make good pets.
- ○ teach you facts about owls.

15 How does blending in help keep owls safe from their enemies?
- ○ Other animals think owls are bigger than they really are.
- ○ Other animals cannot see them very easily.
- ○ Other animals do not like the owls' feathers.

16 If you wanted to tell a fact about owls, what would you say?
- ○ Owls stay the same color.
- ○ Owls are interesting animals.
- ○ Owls have beautiful feathers.

Directions

Write your answer to Question A on the lines below. Base your answer on the two selections you have read.

A Think about the owls in the two selections you have just read. Tell how the owls in "Oscar's Problem" and the ones in "*Whoooo* Has Big Feathers?" are different.

WRITING ACROSS TEXTS

© Pearson Education 2

Directions

Read the letter Sophie wrote to her cousin about something that happened one night. Then answer Numbers 17 through 24.

A Letter to Kathy

Dear Kathy,

You won't believe what I saw last night! I was getting ready for bed when I looked out my window. I saw two yellow lights in the big maple tree. They were about three inches apart. Suddenly, they went off and then on again. I kept staring at the spot and then decided to turn off the light in my room. As my eyes got used to the darkness, I saw that the two lights were really two eyes. I was looking at a bird that was as big as a basketball. I know now that it was a great gray owl. I looked it up in my father's bird book this morning.

The owl's face looked big and round like a full moon. In the middle was a yellow beak that pointed straight down. Its feathers had spots of gray and black and white and brown. The owl didn't move for about twenty minutes. I couldn't stop looking at it. I couldn't tell if it saw me or not. Finally, it jumped off the branch and flew away. Its wings made almost no sound, just a soft whoosh, whoosh, whoosh.

I wish I had taken a photo of the owl. I'll try to make a painting of what he looked like before I forget. The next time you come to visit, I'll show you the painting.

Have fun in school and write back soon. Tell me about something you've seen that made you stand still and look.

Your cousin,
Sophie

17 **The author used the words** *whoosh, whoosh, whoosh* **to make you**
- ○ feel the softness of an owl's feathers.
- ○ picture the owl's yellow eyes.
- ○ hear the sound of an owl flying.

18 **You can tell that Sophie**
- ○ does not like birds.
- ○ likes to send and get letters.
- ○ is afraid of the dark.

19 Where was Sophie when she saw the owl?

- ○ in her bedroom
- ○ at the playground
- ○ in her yard

20 What change would make this selection a fantasy?

- ○ Sophie takes a photo of the owl.
- ○ Sophie flies away with the owl.
- ○ Sophie calls Kathy on the phone.

21 What made the two lights in the tree look like they were going off and on?

- ○ The owl was sleeping in the tree.
- ○ The owl was blinking its eyes.
- ○ The owl was flying away.

22 Sophie compared the owl's size to

- ○ a maple tree.
- ○ a book about birds.
- ○ a basketball.

23 What did Sophie do first?

- ○ She saw lights in the tree.
- ○ She wrote a letter to Kathy.
- ○ She looked in a bird book.

24 Sophie planned to paint a picture of the owl because she wanted

- ○ her father to be proud of her.
- ○ the owl to come back to the tree.
- ○ Kathy to see how the owl looked.

Directions

Write your answer to Question B on the lines below. Base your answer on "*Whoooo* Has Big Feathers?" and "A Letter to Kathy."

B Use the information from "*Whoooo* Has Big Feathers?" and Sophie's letter to think about two kinds of owls: a snowy owl and a great gray owl. First tell how these two owls are alike. Then describe the ways they are not the same.

© Pearson Education 2

Directions
Mark your answer choice for Numbers 25 through 33.

25 Sophie saw two yellow lights in a tree. She kept <u>staring</u> at the spot.

What does <u>staring</u> mean?

- ○ flying away
- ○ looking hard
- ○ shining a light

26 Which of these words is a compound word?

- ○ basketball
- ○ animal
- ○ darkness

27 Oscar was sleepy, but the band at his party was <u>loud</u>.

Which word means the opposite of <u>loud</u>?

- ○ funny
- ○ fast
- ○ quiet

28 The word <u>branch</u> has many meanings.

When Oscar sits on an oak <u>branch</u>, the word means

- ○ part of a tree.
- ○ part of a river.
- ○ to divide into many parts.

29 There is a <u>legend</u> that says it's good luck to find an owl feather in the woods.

A <u>legend</u> is something that people

○ use to build houses.

○ tell each other.

○ cook and eat.

30 Oscar danced <u>slowly</u>.

The word <u>slowly</u> tells

○ where he danced.

○ when he danced.

○ how he danced.

31 Sophie wrote, "Tell me about something you've seen that made you stand <u>still</u> and look."

What does <u>still</u> mean in this sentence?

○ yet

○ until the present

○ without moving

32 An owl's feathers are the same colors as its <u>habitat</u>.

A <u>habitat</u> is

○ what the owl eats.

○ where the owl lives.

○ the other animals that live near the owl.

GO ON

33 Like coats, feathers keep owls <u>warm</u>.

Which word is the opposite of <u>warm</u>?

○ dry

○ safe

○ cool

PART 3: PHONICS

Directions
Mark your answer choice for Numbers 34 through 51.

34 The moon lit the <u>night</u>.

What word has the same sound as the <u>igh</u> in <u>night</u>?

- ○ hills
- ○ mice
- ○ thick

35 Some owls have <u>brown</u> feathers.

What word has the same sound as the <u>ow</u> in <u>brown</u>?

- ○ sound
- ○ too
- ○ throw

36 Aunt Opal served a mouse <u>stew</u>.

What word has the same sound as the <u>ew</u> in <u>stew</u>?

- ○ hunt
- ○ turn
- ○ hoot

37 Oscar was a <u>happy</u> owl.

What word is the opposite of <u>happy</u>?

- ○ rehappy
- ○ happiness
- ○ unhappy

GO ON

38 Sophie wished she had taken a <u>photo</u> of the owl.

What word has the same beginning sound as <u>photo</u>?

○ party

○ funny

○ puffy

39 Owls <u>sleep</u> all day.

What word has the same sound as the <u>ee</u> in <u>sleep</u>?

○ blend

○ sneak

○ feathers

40 The owl's beak <u>pointed</u> down.

What word has the same sound as the <u>oi</u> in <u>pointed</u>?

○ joy

○ paint

○ round

41 Owls have thick feathers <u>close</u> to their bodies.

What word has the same sound as the <u>o</u> in <u>close</u>?

○ coat

○ mouse

○ lose

42 Oscar's friend yelled, "Start <u>tapping</u> those toes!"

What is the base word of <u>tapping</u>?

○ pin

○ tap

○ ping

43 How is the word <u>suddenly</u> correctly divided into syllables?

○ sud den ly

○ sudd enl y

○ su dden ly

44 Owls are <u>big</u> birds.

Which word means <u>more big</u>?

○ biggest

○ bigger

○ bigly

45 In the morning, the sun <u>peeked</u> over the hills.

Which of these means the same as <u>peeked</u>?

○ are peeking

○ did peek

○ will peek

46 Owls' feathers blend in so other animals <u>can't</u> see them.

Which means the same as <u>can't</u>?

○ can do

○ did not

○ cannot

47 Sophie wrote about the <u>darkness</u> outside her window.

What is the base word of <u>darkness</u>?

○ dark

○ ark

○ ness

GO ON

48 Sophie wrote, "Tell me about something you've seen."

Which means the same as you've?

○   you are

○   you have

○   you will

49 Sophie didn't know what she was seeing at first.

Which word has the same beginning sound as know?

○   name

○   cow

○   kite

50 At about midnight, Oscar felt sleepy.

What does midnight mean?

○   the end of the night

○   the beginning of the night

○   the middle of the night

51 Owls are wrapped in a layer of soft, thick feathers.

Which word has the same beginning sound as wrapped?

○   water

○   winter

○   really

© Pearson Education 2

PART 4: GRAMMAR, USAGE, MECHANICS

Directions
Mark your answer choice for Numbers 52 through 60.

For Numbers 52 through 56, choose the word that best completes the sentence.

52 Owls _____ mice and squirrels.

  ○ eaten   ○ eats   ○ eat

53 Kathy and _____ saw the large owl.

  ○ I   ○ me   ○ her

54 An owl's feather is _____ than a robin's.

  ○ big   ○ bigger   ○ biggest

55 Owls in meadows _____ tan.

  ○ am   ○ is   ○ are

56 The owl _____ very loud.

  ○ were   ○ was   ○ are

57 Which sentence is written correctly?

  ○ Some owls have white feathers and, others have brown feathers.

  ○ Some owls have white feathers and others have brown feathers.

  ○ Some owls have white feathers, and others have brown feathers.

GO ON

58 **Which sentence is written correctly?**

○ When Sophie saw the owl, she said, "Wow!"

○ "When Sophie saw the owl, she said, Wow!"

○ When Sophie saw the owl, she said, Wow?

59 **Which sentence is written correctly?**

○ We saw owls, robins crows and hawks.

○ We saw owls, robins, crows and, hawks.

○ We saw owls, robins, crows, and hawks.

60 **Which sentence is written correctly?**

○ The owls feathers are gray.

○ The owl's feathers are gray.

○ The owls's feathers are gray.

PART 5: WRITING

PROMPT

In "A Letter to Kathy," Sophie looked at an owl for twenty minutes. Describe something you've looked at for a long time. Write so your reader can imagine where you were and what you saw.

CHECKLIST FOR WRITERS

_____ Did I plan my paper before I started writing?

_____ Did I tell about something that I looked at for a long time?

_____ Did I tell where I was?

_____ Did I use sense words to tell what I saw, heard, smelled, tasted, or touched?

_____ Do my sentences make sense?

_____ Do my sentences begin with capital letters?

_____ Do my sentences end with the correct end marks?

_____ Did I check my spelling?

_____ Did I make sure my paper is the way I want readers to read it?